OUR WORLD TODAY
People, Places, and Issues

Unit 3 Asia

Glencoe
McGraw-Hill

New York, New York   Columbus, Ohio   Chicago, Illinois   Peoria, Illinois   Woodland Hills, California

BOOK ORGANIZATION

Glencoe offers resources that accompany *Our World Today: People, Places, and Issues* to expand, enrich, review, and assess every lesson you teach and for every student you teach. Now Glencoe has organized its many resources for the way you teach.

How This Book is Organized

Each unit resources book offers blackline masters at unit, chapter, and section levels for each unit. Each book is divided into three parts—unit-based resources, chapter-based resources, and section-based resources. Glencoe has included tabs at the side of every activity page in this book to help you navigate.

Unit-Based Resources

We have organized this book so that all unit resources appear in the first part of the unit resources books. Although you may choose to use the specific activities at any time during the course of unit study, Glencoe has placed these resources up front so that you can review your options.

Chapter-Based and Section-Based Resources

Chapter-based resources follow the unit materials. For example, in the Unit 1 Resources booklet Chapter 1 blackline masters appear immediately following Unit 1 materials. The materials appear in the order you teach—Chapter 1 activities; Chapter 1, Section 1 activities; Chapter 1, Section 2 activities; and so on. Following the end of the last section activity for Chapter 1, the Chapter 2 resources appear.

A Complete Answer Key

A complete answer key appears at the back of this book. This answer key includes answers for every activity in the book in the order in which the activities appear in the book.

Glencoe/McGraw-Hill

A Division of The **McGraw·Hill** Companies

Send all inquiries to:
Glencoe/McGraw-Hill
8787 Orion Place
Columbus, Ohio 43240-4027

ISBN 0-07-829381-0

Printed in the United States of America

2 3 4 5 6 7 8 9 10 024 08 07 06 05 04 03

TABLE OF CONTENTS

TABLE OF CONTENTS, CONTINUED

TO THE TEACHER

The Total Package—Our World Today: People, Places, and Issues Classroom Resources

Glencoe's Unit Resources books are packed with activities for the varied needs of all of your students. They include the following activities.

Activities Found in Unit Resources Booklets

- **Regional Atlas Activities**

  These activities enable students to work with the information in the Regional Atlas sections of the student textbook. The activities require students to focus on political and physical maps, charts and graphs, and facts about cultural geography related to each region of the world.

- **Economics and Geography Activities**

  These interdisciplinary activities provide students with the opportunity to analyze and interpret geographical concepts and maps in relation to economics and the economies of the world's regions. The activities are designed to help students appreciate how economics and geography are interrelated.

- **History and Geography Activities**

  These interdisciplinary activities provide students with the opportunity to analyze and interpret maps in relation to historical events. Students are required to practice using geography skills as an aid to understanding history.

- **Environmental Case Studies**

  These case studies provide students with the opportunity to actively explore environmental issues that affect each of the world's regions. Case studies include critical thinking questions and activities designed to extend students' knowledge and appreciation of environmental challenges.

- **Citizenship Activities: Geography and Your Community**

  These application activities give students the opportunity to participate in their communities. The activities involve students in grassroots community projects that may have national or international implications. The projects help students understand how geography affects their own lives on a daily basis. The projects also show students how they can use their communities as resources for becoming geographically informed persons.

- **World Literature Readings**

  These readings provide students with the opportunity to read literature by or about people who live in each of the world's geographic regions. Each selection is preceded by background information and a guided reading suggestion, and followed by comprehension and critical thinking questions.

- **Vocabulary Activities**

  These review and reinforcement activities help students to master unfamiliar terms used in the student edition. The worksheets emphasize identification of word meanings and provide visual and kinesthetic reinforcement of language skills.

- **Cooperative Learning Activities**

  These extension activities offer students clear management directions for working together on a variety of activities that enrich prior learning.

- **Chapter Map Activities**

  These activities include 89 reproducible outline maps, which can be used for a variety of purposes. Twenty-five pages of teacher strategies are included that offer suggestions for using the reproducible maps in the classroom.

- **Chapter Skills Activities**

  These reinforcement activities correspond to the skills lessons presented in each student textbook chapter. The activities give students the opportunity to gain additional skills practice.

- **Reteaching Activities**

  These are a variety of activities designed to enable students to visualize the connections among facts in their textbook. Graphs, charts, tables, and concept maps are among the many types of graphic organizers used.

- **Critical Thinking Skills Activities**

  Critical thinking skills are important to students and to their roles as future voting citizens because they provide the tools to live and work in an ever-changing world. These activities show students how to use information to make judgments, develop their own ideas, and apply what they have learned to new situations.

- **Map and Graph Skills Activities**

  These activities help students develop and practice map- and graphic-based skills. These activities develop the map and graph skills that will help students become geographically informed persons.

- **Reading and Writing Skills Activities**

  These activities help students develop and practice reading and writing skills. These activities are designed to help students not only develop geography skills, but to enable students to apply, relate, interpret, analyze, compare, organize, and write about geography facts and concepts.

- **GeoLab Activities**

  These activities give students the opportunity to explore, through hands-on experience, the various geographic topics presented in the textbook.

- **Enrichment Activities**

  These activities introduce students to content that is different from, but related to, the themes, ideas, and information in the student textbook. Enrichment activities help students develop a broader and deeper understanding of the physical world and global community.

- **Guided Reading Activities**

  These activities provide help for students who are having difficulty comprehending the student text. Students fill in missing information in the guided reading outlines, sentence completion activities, or other information-organizing exercises as they read the textbook.

OUR WORLD TODAY
People, Places, and Issues

Unit 3 Resources

Regional Atlas Activity 3-A

Regional Outline Map Activity

DIRECTIONS: Draw the correct borders on the map for the countries in this region. Then write the name of the country on the correct area.

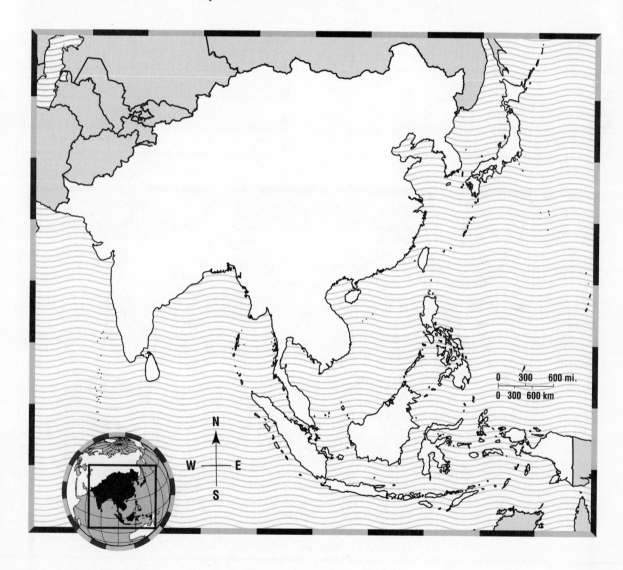

ASIA

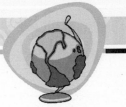

Regional Atlas Activity 3-B

Physical Location Activity

UNIT 3

DIRECTIONS: Identify each physical feature marked by a number on the map.
Then write the correct name on the numbered blanks below.

1. _____   6. _____

2. _____   7. _____

3. _____   8. _____

4. _____   9. _____

5. _____   10. _____

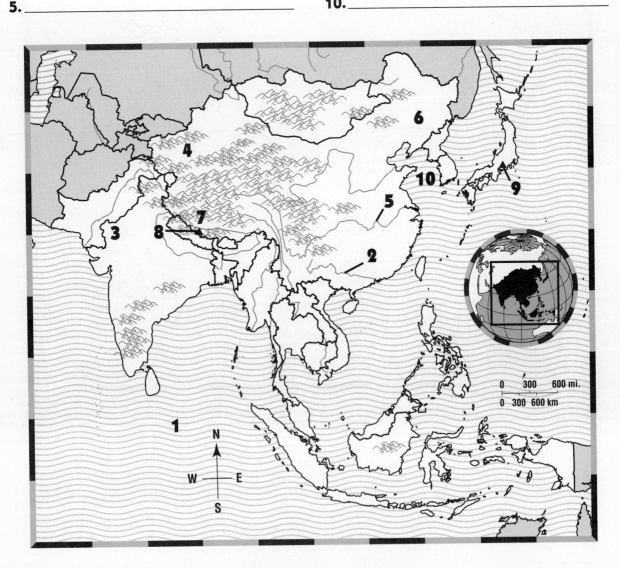

Regional Atlas Activity 3-C

Political Location Activity

DIRECTIONS: Identify each country or territory marked by a number on the map. Then write the correct name on the numbered blanks below.

1. _____

2. _____

3. _____

4. _____

5. _____

6. _____

7. _____

8. _____

9. _____

10. _____

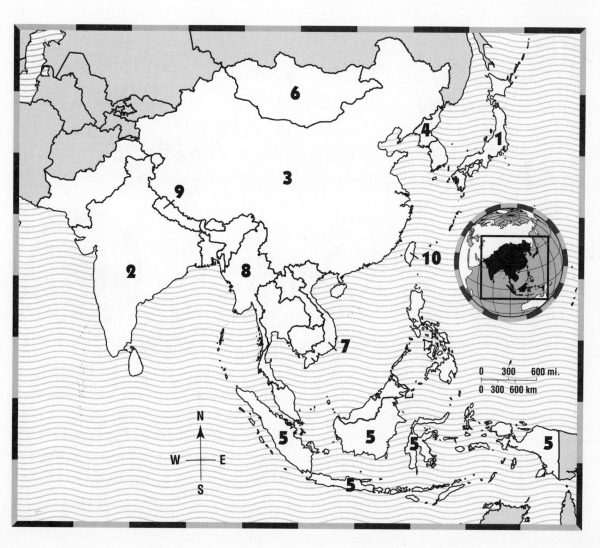

ASIA

Regional Atlas Activity 3-D

City Location Activity

DIRECTIONS: Identify each capital or major city marked by a number on the map. Then write the correct name on the numbered blanks below.

1. _____   6. _____

2. _____   7. _____

3. _____   8. _____

4. _____   9. _____

5. _____   10. _____

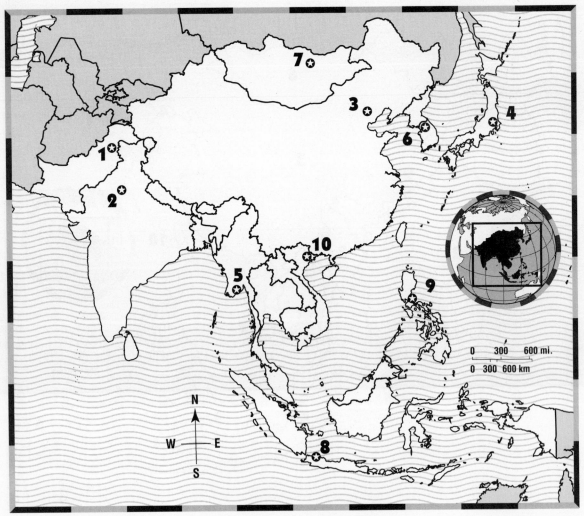

Regional Atlas Activity 3-E

Physical Geography Activity

DIRECTIONS: Find the Unit 3 Regional Atlas physical map on page 134 of your textbook. Then look at the elevation profile below and answer the questions that follow.

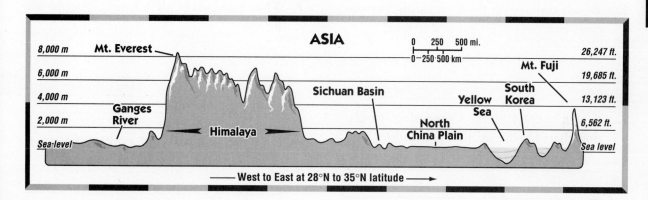

1. What two mountains are shown on this profile? What are their elevations?

   _____

   _____

2. In which countries are these mountains located?

   _____

   _____

   _____

3. What major body of water is shown on this profile? What countries border it?

   _____

   _____

4. Mt. Everest is in the Himalaya. It borders the Plateau of Tibet. What other mountain range borders the Plateau of Tibet?

   _____

   _____

5. What major rivers flow through the North China Plain?

   _____

   _____

   _____

   _____

6. At what latitude is this elevation profile shown?

   _____

   _____

7. Through what countries does this profile run?

   _____

   _____

   _____

   _____

   _____

ASIA

Regional Atlas Activity 3-F

Cultural Geography Activity

DIRECTIONS: Study the Fast Facts on page 137 in the Unit 3 Regional Atlas of your textbook. Then answer the questions below.

1. Which country on the Comparing Population chart has the largest population?

_____

_____

2. Which country on the Comparing Population chart has the smallest population?

_____

_____

3. What is the approximate population of Indonesia?

_____

_____

4. What percentage of the world's people live in each of the following countries?

China: _____

India: _____

Indonesia: _____

Pakistan: _____

Japan: _____

Bangladesh: _____

5. What is the major ethnic group in China?

_____

6. What percentage of China's people live in urban areas?

_____

7. What percentage of Chinese people are literate?

_____

_____

_____

8. What is China's world ranking for gross national product (GNP) per person?

_____

_____

_____

_____

9. What do the world rankings lead you to conclude about life in China?

_____

_____

_____

_____

_____

10. Do you think most people in China use the automobile every day? Why or why not?

_____

_____

_____

_____

_____

_____

Regional Atlas Activity 3-G

Data Table Activity

DIRECTIONS: Study the information in "Country Profiles" on pages 138–140 in the Unit 3 Regional Atlas of your textbook. Determine the 10 most populous countries in Asia. Then fill in the missing data for each country on the table below and answer the questions that follow.

TEN MOST POPULOUS COUNTRIES IN ASIA— MAJOR EXPORTS AND IMPORTS

COUNTRY	POPULATION	EXPORT	IMPORT
	133,500,000	Clothing	
	1,273,300,000		Machinery
India		Gems and jewelry	
		Textiles	Manufactured goods
Japan	127,100,000		
Myanmar			Machinery
		Cotton	Petroleum
	77,200,000		Raw materials
	62,400,000		Machinery
Vietnam		Crude oil	

1. What country in Asia has the largest population? The second-largest population?

_____

_____

2. What product is imported by the most countries in this table?

_____

3. What country exports clothing? Beans?

_____

_____

4. What country on the table both imports and exports machinery?

_____

Name _____ Date _____ Class _____

Economics and Geography Activity 3
Exports and Imports

Exports are goods shipped from one country to another country. A country exports goods for several reasons. Some reasons are:

- It is the primary source of the goods. For example, a country may have minerals that are not available in other countries.
- It produced more goods than it can sell to its own consumers.
- It can produce goods at a lower price than other countries.
- It produces goods of such high quality that other countries are anxious to buy the products.

Imports are goods that are brought into a country from other countries. A country may import goods for the following reasons:

- It does not have similar goods available in its country. For example, the United States imports coffee from Latin America and Africa

because the climate in the United States is not suitable for growing coffee beans.

- It does not produce enough goods in its own markets to meet consumer demand.
- It cannot produce the same quality of goods at the same or a lower price.

What a country exports and imports may change over time. Such a change can be due, in part, to technological developments that create substitute products and new products. For example, a synthetic substitute for silk may reduce the need to import silk products. Consumer demand also may affect exports and imports. For example, the demand for computers and related technology has helped create a new import/export market for many countries.

Government policies may also affect the exports and imports of a country. For example, in order to encourage imports a country can lower its tariff on imports. A **tariff** is a tax placed on

Directions: Use the table below to answer the following questions in the space provided.

U.S. Trade with Selected Asian Countries, 1998 (in millions of dollars)		
Country (Major Export Products)	**U.S. Exports To**	**U.S. Imports From**
Japan (machinery)	$57,831.0	$121,845.0
China (machinery)	14,241.0	71,168.7
Taiwan (textiles)	18,164.5	94,629.0
Malaysia (electronic equipment)	8,957.0	20,959.1
Thailand (manufactured goods)	5,238.6	13,436.4
South Korea (electronic equipment)	16,485.5	23,941.0
Indonesia (textiles)	2,298.9	9,340.6
India (gems and jewelry)	3,564.4	8,237.2
Singapore (computer equipment)	15,693.6	18,355.7
Sri Lanka (textiles)	190.4	1,766.5
Bangladesh (clothing)	318.4	1,845.9

SOURCE: *The World Book of Facts.* (1999), p. 710.

Economics and Geography Activity 3 (continued)

imported products that increases their prices. Lowering trade barriers also allows more imports into a country. A **trade barrier** limits the amount of goods imported into a country. Examples of trade barriers include strict health or safety requirements, limits on the amount of imports into a country, or artificially high prices placed on imported goods. Many of the economically advanced nations such as the United States and Japan favor limiting trade barriers. They want to broaden world markets. Many of the developing countries in Africa, Asia, and Latin America still rely on trade barriers. They want to limit imports in order to create a stronger market for their own industries.

1. From which Asian country did the United States import the most in 1998?

_____

2. To which Asian country did the United States export the most in 1998?

_____

3. For which Asian country was the difference between U.S. imports and exports the greatest in 1998? What was the amount of the difference?

_____

_____

4. For which country was the difference between exports and imports the least?

_____

5. Which Asian countries shown on the table have major exports related to the clothing industry?

_____

_____

6. Which Asian countries on the table have electronic and computer equipment as their major exports?

_____

_____

_____

7. From which three countries did the United States import the least in 1998? What are the major exports of these countries?

_____

_____

_____

_____

8. **Critical Thinking Activity** Trade barriers and tariffs may affect the purchasing power of consumers. Select two or three items that the U.S. imports from Asia. Write a paragraph describing how tariffs or trade barriers might affect what you or other Americans buy. Support your ideas with examples. Be prepared to defend your response.

History and Geography Activity 3

UNIT 3

The Great Wall of China

Some consider the Great Wall of China the eighth wonder of the world. Perhaps it is. It is certainly one of the greatest construction projects in the history of the world.

Fear, not glory, however, was the motivation behind building the wall. The Chinese could live with floods and droughts. They could cope with forest fires and harsh winters. What struck absolute terror in their hearts was one word: Mongols.

The Mongols were a fierce nomadic people who would swoop south from the steppes of Mongolia across the northern border of China and terrorize the people, burn their houses, and steal whatever they could carry back with them. China's armies were useless against the Mongol raiders' lightning fast attacks.

Chinese homes had walls around them. Walls surrounded ancient Chinese cities. Why not build walls to keep the Mongols out? Rulers of different eras tried to build walls to keep the Mongols out. They built hundreds of miles of large earthen walls where the Mongol threat was the greatest. The Mongol raids, however, continued. The walls did not stop the Mongols because the walls were not connected— the Mongols went around the walls.

The first emperor of a united China, Qin Shi Huangdi, decided on a solution that offered, he hoped, permanent protection. In 221 B.C. he ordered that all the existing walls be connected, and that new walls be built to form one long wall. By 206 B.C. workers had constructed 1,550 miles

(2,500 kilometers) of what is now called the Qin Dynasty Great Wall. Time and weather have since eroded the packed mud wall. This wall, though, did not protect China. In fact, the Mongol King, Kublai Khan, not only invaded China, he became emperor in A.D. 1279!

China regained control of the throne in A.D. 1368. Around A.D. 1450 work began on what is now known as the Great Wall of China. It was a new wall in a new location. This wall has lasted because the workers used stone instead of pounded mud. The wall, when finally completed, was 12 feet (3.6 meters) wide and 30 feet (9.1 meters) tall. At one time it stretched at least 4,200 miles (6,700 kilometers) across northern China.

Times have changed. Parts of the Great Wall of China still stand. Now, however, it does not function to keep the enemies of China out. Instead, it has become a wall of friendship, inviting more than 10,000 visitors a day to China to walk along the wall and think of the days when it was China's only protection against the fierce Mongols.

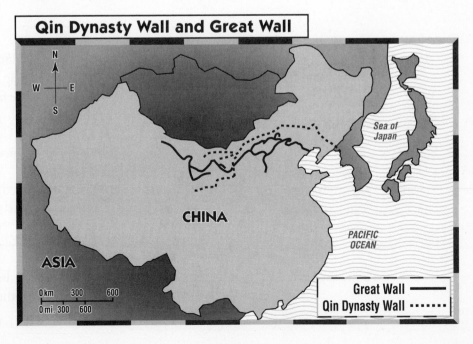

Qin Dynasty Wall and Great Wall

CHINA

Sea of Japan

PACIFIC OCEAN

ASIA

0 km 300 600
0 mi. 300 600

Great Wall ————
Qin Dynasty Wall ∙∙∙∙∙∙∙∙

ASIA

History and Geography Activity 3 (continued)

Directions: Answer the questions below in the spaces provided.

1. Why did the Chinese build the Qin Dynasty Great Wall and the Great Wall of China?

   _____

   _____

   _____

2. Why were the series of earthen walls the Chinese built unsuccessful at keeping the Mongols out?

   _____

   _____

3. When was the Qin Dynasty Wall begun?

   _____

4. How many miles of wall had workers constructed by 206 B.C.?

   _____

5. How do we know that the Qin Dynasty Wall did not keep the Mongols out of China?

   _____

   _____

   _____

6. The Qin Dynasty Wall did not last. Why has the Great Wall lasted?

   _____

   _____

   _____

7. **Making Inferences** Many people risked and lost their lives to build the Great Wall of China. Why do you think they did it?

   _____

   _____

   _____

8. **Drawing Conclusions** China built the Great Wall as a barrier. What barriers have other countries used to keep out invaders?

   _____

   _____

   _____

9. **Analyzing Information** The Great Wall of China twists and turns across thousands of miles of northern China. Why do you think the wall was not built in a straight line?

   _____

   _____

   _____

10. **Mapping Activity** On the map of China on page 5, label the following places: Mongolia, Russia, Kazakhstan, the Gobi, the Yellow Sea, and Beijing. Use the map to answer the following questions.

    a. What prevented the Chinese from building the wall farther east?

    _____

    b. What natural barrier made it unnecessary to extend the wall farther to the west?

    _____

Environmental Case Study 3

Jakarta's Growing Pains

Overview

The city of Jakarta is on the northwest coast of the island of Java in Indonesia. It lies on the Ciliwung River. It is the capital of Indonesia and is a thriving center of trade, business, and education. Each year, many people come to Jakarta from other parts of Indonesia looking for jobs with good pay. Along with people moving to the city, the population of Jakarta has grown due to its high birthrates. Experts predict that by 2015, Jakarta will have nearly double the number of people it had in 1995, and will be the fifth-largest city in the world. Its large population, which has grown rapidly, is causing many problems for Jakarta.

Air Pollution Jakarta has severe air pollution. The biggest source of this pollution is cars. In just eight years, the number of vehicles on the road more than doubled. The second-largest source of air pollution is people burning their garbage. Industrial wastes and cooking on kerosene stoves also contribute to the pollution problem.

The amount of lead in Jakarta's air exceeds the maximum level recommended by the World Health Organization. Most of this lead comes from the leaded fuel used by cars. Many countries have banned lead in gasoline because of its harmful health effects. A 1994 government study warned that lead was affecting the mental development of children in Jakarta. Since then, the problem has gotten worse.

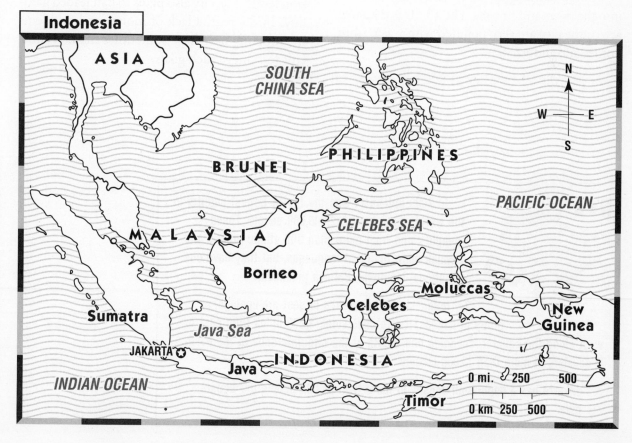

Indonesia

ASIA
Environmental Case Study 3 (continued)

Water Supplies and Pollution Many people in Jakarta do not have access to fresh, clean water. The Dutch, who controlled Indonesia for many years, planned the city's water supply system for a population of less than half a million. In 2000, Jakarta's population was 8.3 million. Piped-in water does not reach many households. Most people take the majority of their water from private wells. People have withdrawn so much water from the ground that the northern part of the city has begun to sink.

Poor people often have neither piped-in water nor wells. They have to buy expensive bottled water to drink. Drinking water is frequently contaminated by waste from septic tanks (underground tanks for home sewage treatment), salt from seawater, and toxic substances from landfills. Many people have to boil their water before drinking it.

Some companies dump pollutants directly into the rivers and streams. The 13 rivers that flow across the city are very polluted with waste from homes and industry.

Waste Disposal Most of Jakarta does not have a modern sewage system of sealed underground pipes that take wastewater to sewage treatment plants. Open ditches take the wastewater, sometimes without treatment, to rivers or the sea. The city collects garbage from about three-quarters of the households. However, Jakarta does not have enough trucks to haul all of the garbage. To get rid of their garbage, some people dump it along the side of the street, while others burn it.

Solutions The city has made many improvements to slum areas. These include building roads, public toilets, health clinics, and schools. Unfortunately, Jakarta's population has grown so much that the city has been unable to keep up with the need for housing. It is laying more water pipelines and plans to build a new sewage system. The government of Jakarta intends to start inspecting cars and requiring them to meet emission levels. The city also plans to ban leaded gasoline. In the past, a lack of money and problems in enforcing laws have sometimes made it difficult to achieve such goals.

1. In 2000 Indonesia was the fourth-largest country in the world, with about 212,000,000 people. These people come from more than 300 ethnic groups and speak more than 200 languages, but they have one national language, Bahasa Indonesia.

2. Indonesia is the world's largest archipelago, or group of islands. It stretches some 3,200 miles from east to west along the Equator, spanning one-eighth of the circumference of the earth. It consists of more than 13,000 islands.

3. Jakarta has a population density of more than 34,000 people per square mile.

ASIA
Environmental Case Study 3 (continued)

HOUSING AND URBAN SPRAWL

Housing is a big problem in Jakarta. Good housing is expensive and hard to find. The city has many slum areas. Some people live in houses made from scraps of metal, cardboard, or wood. Often, there are no schools or hospitals nearby. In crowded slums, diseases like influenza and tuberculosis can spread easily.

The city is becoming so crowded that many poor people are being pushed out of it. Jakarta is facing the problem of urban sprawl (the area taken up by a large or expanding city). Farmland outside the city is being taken over by housing and businesses.

Each day, 6 million people commute to Jakarta from outlying areas in cars, buses, or trains to get to their jobs. There is so much traffic that commuting to work can take more than two hours. Some people spend up to 50 percent of their earnings on transportation, but that is still cheaper than living in the city.

Jakarta's Growing Pains: Review the Facts

Directions: Write the answer to each question in the space provided.

1. What has caused many problems for Jakarta?

_____

_____

_____

2. List two causes of air pollution in Jakarta.

A. _____

B. _____

3. How do people living in the city get their drinking water?

_____

_____

_____

4. Why has the northern part of Jakarta begun to sink?

_____

_____

_____

5. Describe the sewage system in Jakarta.

_____

_____

_____

6. What happens to garbage that is not collected?

_____

_____

_____

7. Explain why housing is a problem in Jakarta.

_____

_____

_____

8. List two improvements Jakarta has made or is planning to make.

A. _____

B. _____

UNIT 3

ASIA
Environmental Case Study 3 (continued)

Make a Model City

Reading the case study has probably given you some ideas about the services a city should offer and how important careful planning is to making a city livable. Plan and create an ideal model city that gives all its citizens a place to live, work, and enjoy leisure time.

What to Do

1. Plan your city. Include areas for housing, business, and recreation. Also plan a good road system and government buildings such as police stations and fire departments.

2. Draw a sketch of how you think your city should be laid out. Look over your sketch and make any necessary changes. Then transfer your drawing to a large sheet of poster board.

3. Using cardboard, glue, and tape, make the buildings in your city. Place the structures in the appropriate areas and then tape them into place.

4. Label the government buildings.

5. Color-code the areas of the city. Use a different color to mark the buildings or area boundaries of each section—residential, commercial, and recreational.

6. Make a color-coded key and attach it to your city plan.

7. Review your plan. Could people live in your city? Are the parts of the city where people might come for business or recreation easy to reach? Can police officers and firefighters get to all parts of the city? Are schools and shopping areas close at hand? Make any necessary changes before you present your model city to the class.

Materials

- poster board
- crayons or markers
- tempera paint
- cardboard
- cellophane tape
- glue

A SKETCH OF A MODEL CITY

Citizenship Activity 3

Careers in the Peace Corps

Why It's Important In places like Nepal, located in the Himalaya, American Peace Corps volunteers help people build a better life. One way the volunteers help is by teaching in local schools. In Nepal, only one-third of the young people attend school. Peace Corps volunteers travel into the remote hills so more young people can receive an education. Volunteers also train the Nepalese to become teachers. In one year alone, volunteers taught 5,000 schoolchildren and trained 1,200 teachers there.

Developing countries (countries that are working toward industrialization) often require the help of wealthier countries in order to build a better life for their people. As citizens of a wealthy country, U.S. Peace Corps volunteers have an opportunity to help people of other countries. You have a similar opportunity to help people in your community. Helping others is part of being a citizen of a community—and a citizen of the world. When you help to make the lives of other people better, you make your own life better.

Background

In 1961 President John F. Kennedy created an organization called the Peace Corps. The purpose of this organization is to promote world peace by helping improve the standard of living for the people of some foreign countries. Volunteers from across the United States work to bring clean water to communities, teach in schools, start new businesses, create better farming methods, and promote better health practices.

Since the beginning of the Peace Corps, more than 155,000 Americans have joined. Volunteers have served in 134 countries, helping the host countries take charge of their own futures.

Questions to Consider

Directions: Answer the questions below on a separate sheet of paper.

1. Do you believe that as a citizen of a wealthy country, you have an obligation to help people of poorer countries? Why or why not?

2. If you could interview a Peace Corps volunteer, what questions would you ask him or her?

3. Why might someone want to join the Peace Corps?

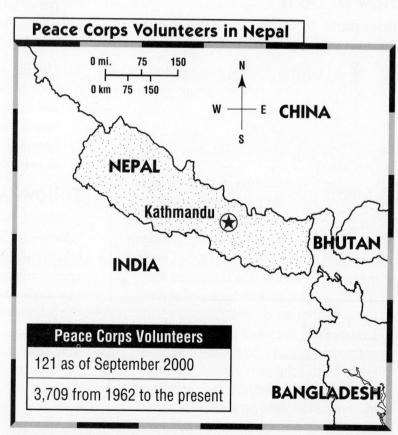

Peace Corps Volunteers in Nepal

Peace Corps Volunteers
121 as of September 2000
3,709 from 1962 to the present

ASIA
Citizenship Activity 3 (continued)

4. Do you think you might want to live in a foreign country to help the people there? Why or why not?

5. Do you think living in a foreign country or learning about people from a foreign country adds to your life? How?

6. What could you do in your community to help Peace Corps volunteers make a difference around the world?

7. What is the first step you could take today toward making a positive difference in your community?

Your Task

Your task is to create a class bulletin board that shows volunteer career opportunities in the Peace Corps.

How to Do It

Directions: Follow the steps below to complete the activity.

1. Use the Internet, library, or write directly to the Peace Corps to learn more about the organization. The Peace Corps has many regional locations. You may also contact the national headquarters in Washington, D.C.

2. Organize into at least five small groups. Name your groups the following: Agriculture, Education, Environment, Health, and Youth Development. Each group should plan a visual presentation about the Peace Corps. The presentation should contain information on the group's title. For example, if the group is named Youth Development, the information in the presentation should be about Peace Corps Youth Development.

3. Divide the classroom bulletin board's space into five sections. Each group is to fill one of the sections.

4. Each group can use magazine cutouts, photographs, markers, paint, construction paper, poster board, colorful ribbon, and other art supplies to create their section of the bulletin board.

5. Use the name of your group as the title of your bulletin board. Write photo captions and other short explanations for the bulletin board. Post the captions and short explanations with the appropriate photographs and drawings.

Follow-Up Activity

Begin a youth "Peace Corps" activity in your community. Plan a class activity that helps your community. For example, if you live in a farming community where foreign workers are employed, you might choose to entertain the children while the parents work in the fields. If there are students in your school who speak English as a second language, you could organize tutoring sessions for those students.

Did You Know?

You must be 18 years old to join the Peace Corps, but there is nothing to stop your parents and grandparents from joining. The oldest Peace Corps member was 86 when he completed his service, and one mother became a volunteer only after her daughter signed up. In January 2002, President George W. Bush announced plans to double the number of Peace Corps volunteers abroad, steering more of them to countries that he believes most misunderstand America.

World Literature Reading 3

UNIT 3

About the Selection The novel, *The Long Season of Rain*, takes place in Korea in 1969. The title refers to *changma,* the Korean word for the rainy season. The author tells about Junehee, the 11-year-old main character and her family. Changhee Uhnni is one of Junehee's sisters. This selection from the book describes their house.

Guided Reading As you read this selection, try to draw a picture in your mind of Junehee's house. Then answer the questions that follow.

Reader's Dictionary

lattice: a framework or structure of crossed wood strips
rice paper: a thin, papery material
eaves: the lower borders of a roof that overhangs a wall

from THE LONG SEASON OF RAIN
by Helen Kim

We were playing jacks with five small stones in the entryway to our house, sheltered from the rain and away from Grandmother. She didn't like us playing jacks in the living area because the stones made marks on the wooden floor, but more so because we were noisy when we played. As all traditional houses in Korea, our house had very little privacy. If we wanted to play loudly or talk away from adults' ears, we had to move away from the main section where the living area joined Grandmother's room and our big room that we shared with Mother and Father.

The wooden lattice sliding doors covered with rice paper in Grandmother's room and our room didn't keep much noise out. We could hear Grandmother reading the Bible in her room with all the doors closed or the telephone conversation in the living area, even if Mother or Grandmother was whispering. We learned to read each other's lips when we didn't want the adults to hear us, and we always tried to play quietly.

More than anyone else, though, Mother knew how to do everything quietly. She could open her clothing cabinet door or slide out her dresser drawer almost without a sound. When she needed to talk to Father, she waited until night and then spoke softly. If she wanted to be alone, she went to the vegetable garden through the little door in the surrounding wall. Sometimes we found her there even in the middle of the winter, when the thickest socks barely kept us warm inside.

We lived in a typical Korean house, though our vegetable garden was not that common. The house was in the shape of a horseshoe, and in the hollow middle was a courtyard with a rose garden where white, pink, and red roses bloomed in early summer. Facing the garden from the living area, the left arm had the kitchen, the pantry/dining room, and our helper's room. The right arm included the storage room, the entrance area, the bathroom and an extra bedroom that became Changhee Uhnni's and mine that summer.

Except for the main section, where we could go from our bedroom to Grandmother's without putting on shoes, the other parts of the house were not internally connected. When it rained, we had to put on our shoes and walk underneath the eaves in order to go to the kitchen or the bathroom.

The house and the grounds were surrounded by a protective wall. All that could be seen from the street was the gray tiled roof that sloped down, turned up in the corners, and jutted out from the main structure. During *changma*, spurts of water gushed from the jade-colored gutter that ran along the tiled roof.

Source: Excerpt from *The Long Season of Rain* by Helen Kim. Copyright © 1996 by Helen Kim. Reprinted by permission of Henry Holt and Company, LLC.

Analyzing the Reading

1. What does Junehee's house, like all traditional Korean houses, lack?

_____

_____

2. What shape is Junehee's house?

_____

_____

3. Critical Thinking What is a major difference between traditional Korean houses and houses or apartments in the United States?

_____

_____

_____

World Literature Reading 3 (continued)

About the Selection The novel *Shabanu* takes place in present-day Pakistan. Shabanu is the main character. She lives in the Cholistan Desert with her nomadic family. At the beginning of the book, her family is struggling because it has not rained for two years. They are nearly out of water and are preparing to travel to a village with a deep well. Much to their relief, it rains the night before they are to leave. This selection tells about the day after the rain. Phulan is Shabanu's sister and Guluband is her camel.

Reader's Dictionary

wash: a broad sweep of thin color
toba: freshwater pond that serves as a water supply for nomads
tethered: tied, but able to move within a certain radius
pogh: thorny desert plant that camels like to eat

Guided Reading Notice how Shabanu describes her homeland. Also notice how her homeland makes her feel. Then answer the questions that follow.

---

from SHABANU, DAUGHTER OF THE WIND
by Suzanne Fisher Staples

The sun spreads an orange wash across the swept mud floor, and mellow points of light glint from Mama's silver bracelets. I am impatient to take Guluband to the *toba* to see how much rain has collected. I take the goatskin and water pots to where he stands tethered to a wooden stake at the edge of the courtyard.

"Phulan, stop daydreaming and bring more milk," says Mama. Phulan opens the rough wooden door to a baked mud mound at the edge of the court-yard, where the camels' milk will keep cool through the day. She reaches inside and pulls out a round earthen pot. I rub Guluband's nose and slip a piece of brown sugar under his lip. He grunts softly as I take his reins.

"Uushshshsh," I say softly. "Uuuushshshshshsh." He dips his great head, roaring a protest as he always does, perhaps to let the world know he is a camel. He folds his front legs under him and kneels, sinking quietly to the ground. I fling the goatskin over his shoulder and attach the earthen water pots to his wooden saddle. I climb up behind his hump and twine my fingers into curls of rough brown hair to hold my seat while he lurches to his feet.

Guluband lifts his head and we survey the gray desert, rising and falling like the Arabian Sea beyond the dunes, with misty mounds of *pogh* and thorn trees floating for hundreds of miles around. I squint and look at the dunes on the horizon, which is inside India.

Sometimes our animals wander across the border, and when I go to fetch them I look hard to see how it differs from our Pakistan. But the same dunes roll on into India, and I can't tell for certain exactly where Pakistan ends and India begins.

UNIT 3

ASIA

World Literature Reading 3 (continued)

Without a signal from me, Guluband turns toward the *toba*, his feet whispering in the powdery sand, his powerful legs unfolding and stretching in loping rhythm as ancient as the desert. I think of leaving Cholistan, and my chest swells with a pain so deep it closes my throat and sends tears to my eyes.

"Guluband, *ooh chumroo, tori totoo, mithoo* Guluband," I sing to him softly. His furry ears swivel backward and his feet pick up the rhythm of my voice, the brass bracelets around his legs jangling. His knees lift against his chest, his back legs striding twice for every step of a foreleg. His neck absorbs the rhythm, his head high and steady, and I feel there is nowhere else so grand on earth.

Source: Excerpt from *Shabanu, Daughter of the Wind* by Suzanne Fisher Staples. Copyright © 1989 by Suzanne Fisher Staples. Reprinted by permission of Alfred A. Knopf Children's Books, a division of Random House, Inc.

Analyzing the Reading

1. What does Shabanu say the gray desert rises and falls like?

_____

_____

2. What differences does Shabanu see in the landscape across the border in India?

_____

_____

3. Critical Thinking Shabanu loves her desert home. Find two excerpts from this selection that support this statement.

_____

_____

_____

4. Critical Thinking Name some differences you can find between Shabanu's nomadic way of life and your way of life here in the United States.

_____

_____

_____

_____

Chapter 5 Resources

SOUTH ASIA

Vocabulary Activity 5

CHAPTER 5

DIRECTIONS: Fill in the Blanks Select a term to fill each blank in the paragraphs below.

subcontinent

monsoon

jute

cottage industry

castes

reincarnation

cyclone

pesticides

dzong

People in India do many jobs. Some are farmers who grow crops such as tea, sugarcane, and cotton. Another important crop is (**1**) _____, the fiber used in making rope. Some Indian people may work in a factory, while others operate a (**2**) _____

_____ in their home or village, making beautiful silk or cotton cloth.

South Asia is called a (**3**) _____ because it is a large landmass that is part of a continent, but is distinct from it. Seasons in South Asia are affected by (**4**) _____ winds that bring dry air part of the year and moist air another part. After the monsoon season ends, an intense storm called a (**5**) _____ may cause damage with high winds and heavy rains.

The rivers in South Asia are important sources of water and means of travel. In India, burning coal, industrial wastes, and (**6**) _____ have polluted much of the river water.

High in the Himalaya, Bhutan's people follow the Buddhist religion. If you visit the mountains, you may see a (**7**) _____, a Buddhist center of prayer and study. These centers have shaped Bhutan's art and culture.

Hinduism is the religion followed by most of India's people. Hinduism organized India's society into groups called (**8**) _____. Hinduism teaches that after the body dies, the soul is reborn. This process, called (**9**) _____, is repeated until the soul reaches perfection.

Cooperative Learning Activity 5

Monsoon Season

Background

The word *monsoon* comes from the Arabic word for time or season. Geographers use *monsoon* to describe a seasonal change in wind patterns that takes place in South and East Asia. The monsoon season typically begins with a drought followed by heavy rains. In India, seasonal monsoons provide many benefits, but they can also be very destructive. They are a basic part of people's lives and the economy in India.

Group Directions

1. You have been asked to describe and explain monsoons to a group of students and their teacher so that they will understand monsoons' significance to the people of India. You will present your information in an oral report to this group.

2. Use Chapter 5 and library resources or the Internet to learn about the benefits of monsoons, as well as the harm they cause.

3. Collect pictures from magazines, newspapers, or the Internet that show the results of India's monsoons.

4. Use what you learn to create and give an oral report. If possible, make a multimedia presentation, using computer slides or videos showing pictures, charts, and maps about monsoon activity.

5. Consider which of the following information you will present about India's monsoons:

causes and seasonal patterns	benefits
how people adapt	destructive results

Organizing the Group

1. **Decision Making** Decide what information each member of the group will look for. Use the topics in the box to help make assignments.

2. **Group Work/Decision Making** Meet with your group and brainstorm the kinds of information and pictures you want to include in your oral report. Be sure to include how and where monsoons form, their typical

Cooperative Learning Activity 5 (continued)

appearance, and their effects. If you have access to multimedia tools, discuss how you will do your presentation. Then divide up the tasks for creating your multimedia presentation.

3. **Individual Work** Research your topic. Collect pictures and draw illustrations. Prepare your assigned parts of the presentation.

4. **Additional Group Work** Share your research with the group. Together, organize your group's information and illustrations into an oral presentation. Decide who will present each part of the report so that all members have a role in the presentation.

5. **Group Sharing** Groups should take turns giving their oral reports to the rest of the class. Together, discuss the advantages and disadvantages of having seasonal monsoons.

Group Process Questions

- What is the most important thing you learned about India's monsoons from this activity?

- What part of the project did you enjoy most?

- If you did a multimedia presentation, what special problems did this form of report pose for the group?

- How did you solve the problems?

- How was it helpful to work with others?

Quick Check

1. Was the goal of the assignment clear at all times?

_____

2. Did you have problems working well together? If so, how did you solve them?

_____

3. Was your group's presentation as good as you thought it would be? How could it be improved?

_____

Chapter Map Activity 5

Teaching Strategy

India and six of its neighbors—Pakistan, Bangladesh, Nepal, Bhutan, Sri Lanka, and the Maldives—make up the region known as South Asia. South Asia is sometimes referred to as a subcontinent—a large landmass that is part of another continent yet distinct from it.

Regional and Political Maps

Place Location Activity

Reproduce the regional map for each student. Ask students to:

- Label the following countries and their boundaries: Pakistan, India, Nepal, Bhutan, Bangladesh, Sri Lanka, Maldives.
- Trace the following rivers: Indus, Ganges, Brahmaputra, Krishna.
- Label the following bodies of water: Indian Ocean, Arabian Sea, Bay of Bengal.
- With an arrow, indicate on your map in what direction the United States is from this region.

Reproduce the political map for each student. Ask students to:

- Label the countries and bodies of water. *(See the list of countries and bodies of water for the regional map.)*
- Mark and label the national capital and major cities of each country. *(Remind students to include a map key.)*

Discussing the Maps

1. True or false: Sri Lanka is part of India. *(False; Sri Lanka is an independent nation.)*
2. In which direction would you travel if you journeyed in a straight line from Dhaka to Kathmandu? Through which countries would you travel? *(You would travel northwest and would pass through Bangladesh, India, and Nepal.)*
3. Name the bodies of water that border India. *(Arabian Sea, Indian Ocean, and Bay of Bengal)*
4. Which two South Asian capital cities lie the farthest apart? What is the approximate straight-line distance between them? *(Male, Maldives, and Islamabad, Pakistan, are the South Asian capital cities that lie the farthest apart—about 1,950 miles [3,120 km].)*
5. How many South Asian countries are landlocked? Name them. *(Two South Asian countries are landlocked: Nepal and Bhutan.)*

Physical and Capitals and Major Cities Maps

Place Location Activity

Reproduce the physical map for each student. Ask students to:

- Label the countries, rivers, and bodies of water. *(See the list for the regional map.)*
- Mark and label the major cities of each country.
- Label the following: Andaman Islands, Western Ghats, Eastern Ghats, Deccan Plateau, Great Indian Desert, Ganges Plain, Hindu Kush, Karakoram Range, Himalaya.

Reproduce the capitals and major cities map for each student. Ask students to:

- Label the countries.
- Label the capital and major cities of each country.

Discussing the Maps

1. Name the two mountain ranges that make up India's northern border and separate South Asia from the rest of Asia. *(Karakoram Range and the Himalaya)*
2. The Indus River flows primarily through which South Asian country? *(Pakistan)*
3. True or false: Part of India lies east of Bangladesh. *(true)*
4. What is the source of both the Ganges and Brahmaputra Rivers? *(the Himalaya)*

APPLYING GEOGRAPHY SKILLS

Mapping the World's Highest Mountains

You may use the following activity as a cooperative learning activity or extra credit project.

The northern ranges of the Himalaya and Karakoram contain the highest mountains on Earth. All 14 mountains in the world that are higher than 8,000 meters can be found in this region. Divide the class into two groups and assign seven of the following peaks to each: Mount Everest, K2, Kangchenjunga, Lhotse, Makalu, Cho Oyu, Dhaulagiri, Manaslu, Nanga Parbat, Annapurna, Gasherbrum I, Broad Peak, Gasherbrum II, Shisha Pangma. Students should use copies of their physical maps to indicate the location and height of each mountain.

Chapter Map Activity 5

CHAPTER 5

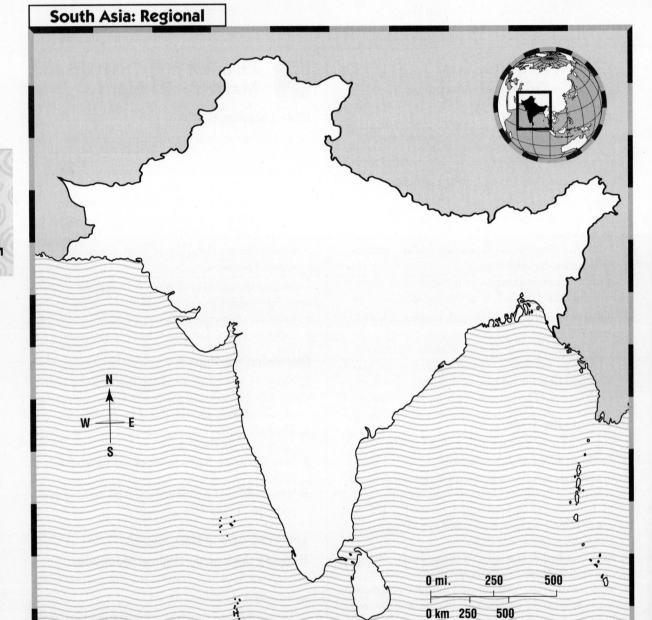

South Asia: Regional

N
W — E
S

0 mi.   250   500
0 km   250   500

Chapter Map Activity 5

South Asia: Political

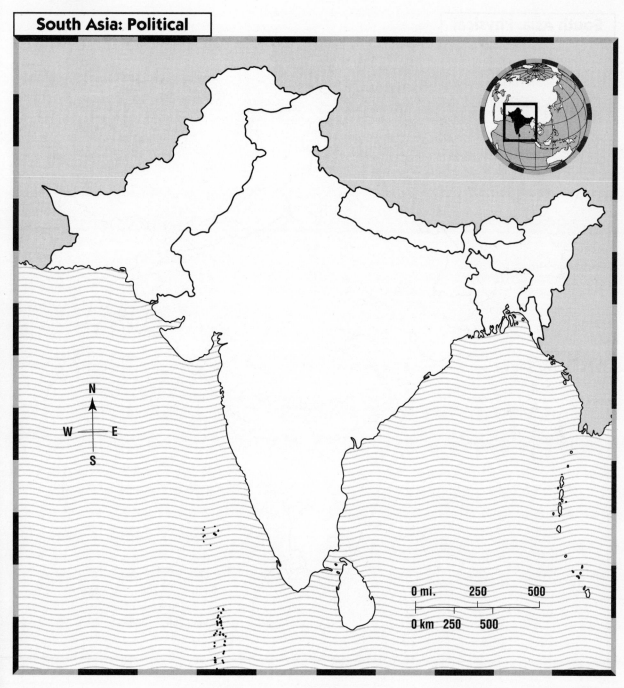

SOUTH ASIA

Chapter Map Activity 5

South Asia: Physical

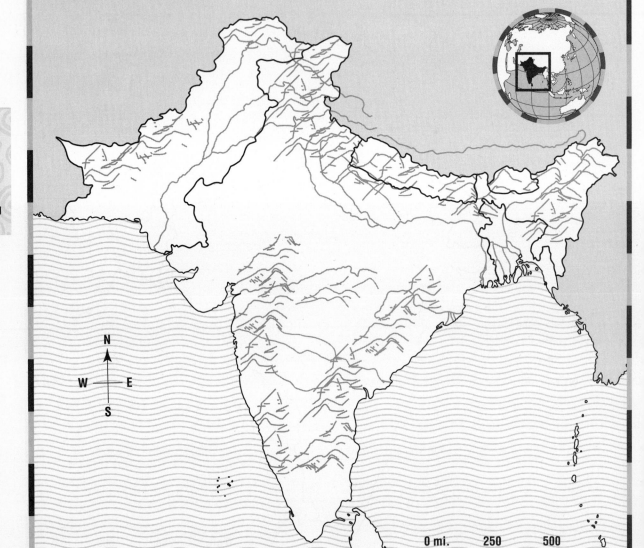

Chapter Map Activity 5

South Asia: Capitals and Major Cities

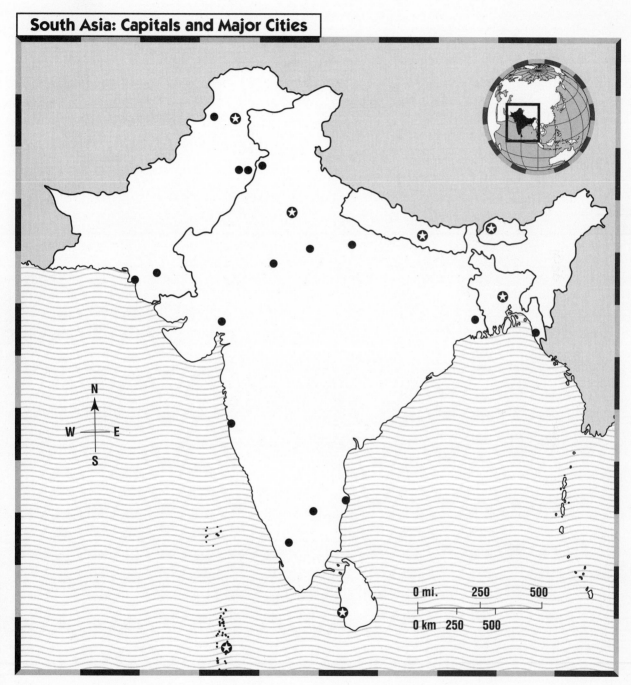

South Asia: Capitals and Major Cities

Chapter Skills Activity 5

Reading a Circle Graph

 ## Learning the Skill

A circle graph is also called a pie chart. In a circle graph, the complete circle represents a whole group or 100 percent. The circle is divided into "slices," or wedge-shaped sections representing parts of the whole. To read a circle graph, first read the title of the circle graph to find out what the subject is. Then study the labels or the key to see what each segment or "slice" of the circle represents. Finally, compare the sizes of the circle slices. This will tell you how one slice of the pie compares to another slice.

Practicing the Skill

Directions: Look at the graphs below to answer the questions that follow.

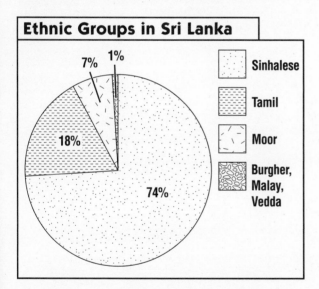

Ethnic Groups in Sri Lanka

7% 1%
18%
74%

Sinhalese
Tamil
Moor
Burgher, Malay, Vedda

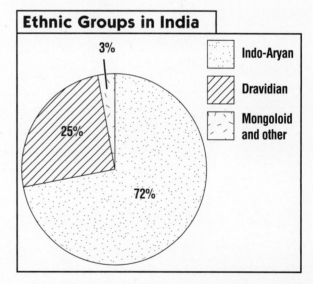

Ethnic Groups in India

3%
25%
72%

Indo-Aryan
Dravidian
Mongoloid and other

1. What is the subject of the circle graphs? _____

2. What is the largest ethnic group in India? _____

3. Which country has more ethnic groups? _____

4. What percentage of people in Sri Lanka are Sinhalese? _____

Applying the Skill

Directions: Take a poll of 10 classmates to find out what vegetable each hates most. Create a circle graph with your results on a separate sheet of paper.

Reteaching Activity 5

South Asia is a subcontinent because it is like a continent, only smaller. Six countries occupy this landmass. The subcontinent has a varied, spectacular landscape. The people who live here practice several religions and follow unique cultural traditions. Several civil wars have resulted because of religious and ethnic differences.

DIRECTIONS: Filling in the Blanks On the line before each description below, write the name of the country being described.

- Pakistan
- Sri Lanka
- Bhutan
- Bangladesh
- India
- Nepal

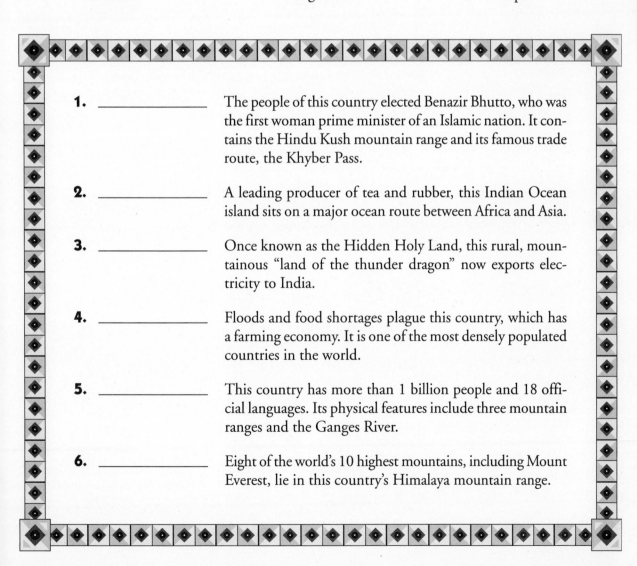

1. _____ The people of this country elected Benazir Bhutto, who was the first woman prime minister of an Islamic nation. It contains the Hindu Kush mountain range and its famous trade route, the Khyber Pass.

2. _____ A leading producer of tea and rubber, this Indian Ocean island sits on a major ocean route between Africa and Asia.

3. _____ Once known as the Hidden Holy Land, this rural, mountainous "land of the thunder dragon" now exports electricity to India.

4. _____ Floods and food shortages plague this country, which has a farming economy. It is one of the most densely populated countries in the world.

5. _____ This country has more than 1 billion people and 18 official languages. Its physical features include three mountain ranges and the Ganges River.

6. _____ Eight of the world's 10 highest mountains, including Mount Everest, lie in this country's Himalaya mountain range.

Critical Thinking Skills Activity 5

Making Generalizations

SOCIAL STUDIES OBJECTIVE: Analyze information by making generalizations.

 ## Learning the Skill

A broad statement drawn from a group of facts about a topic is called a generalization. You make **generalizations** by starting with a few examples of a specific characteristic in someone, something, or a group. Then you form a broader opinion or conclusion based on that characteristic. As an example, you notice that the first few days of September have been rainy. You could make the generalization that it is going to be a very wet fall season. As another example, you see a few pictures of Indian women wearing nose-rings. You could generalize that most Indian women wear jewelry in their noses. Both of these generalizations may or may not be true. They are merely generalizations based on a few specific facts or instances. To make a generalization you first observe a few factors, then you make a much larger statement about the group of those factors. To be valid, a generalization must be supported by evidence that is logical and factual. To make valid generalizations, follow these steps:

- Identify the subject matter.

- Collect factual information and examples relevant to the topic.

- Identify similarities among the facts.

- Say to yourself, "if these are true, then it must follow that. . . "

- Put the specifics together and make a generalization that states a relationship and is consistent with most of the supporting facts.

Applying the Skill

Directions: Read the following specific information about India and Pakistan.

INDIA

- India has slightly more than 1 billion people.
- About 80 percent of India's people are Hindus and 14 percent are Muslims.
- The people of India speak 18 major languages and more than 1,000 other local languages.
- About 70 percent of India's people live in rural villages.
- The literacy rate is 52 percent: males—65.5 percent, females—37.7 percent.

PAKISTAN

- Pakistan has slightly more than 146 million people.
- About 97 percent of Pakistan's people are Muslims.
- The people of Pakistan speak three major languages.
- About 70 percent of Pakistan's people live in rural villages.
- The literacy rate is 37.8 percent: males—50 percent, females—24.4 percent.

CHAPTER 5

37

SOUTH ASIA
Critical Thinking Skills Activity 5 (continued)

Circle the letters of the following statements that are reasonable generalizations about India and/or Pakistan:

A. Both Indians and Pakistanis are religious people.

B. Muslims who live in rural villages are more educated than Hindus who live in cities.

C. In both cultures, the women are less literate than the men.

D. Indians, in general, are 1,000 times more talkative than Pakistanis.

E. With so many people living in rural villages, India's cities are not crowded.

F. Improving reading skills should be a priority for both countries.

G. There are many more Indians than Pakistanis.

Practicing the Skill

Directions: Read the information about Bangladesh. Then answer the questions that follow by circling the letter of each correct answer.

> Bangladesh has nearly 126 million people living in an area about the size of Wisconsin. It suffers from severe overpopulation. Although Bangladesh's economy depends on farming, many people are landless and forced to farm land that is prone to flooding. Monsoons and cyclones cause flooding during the summer. Farmers raise rice, sugarcane, and jute. However, few of them have modern farming tools or use modern farming methods. There is limited access to drinkable water. Diseases carried by water are extremely common. Water pollution, especially of fishing areas, results from the use of commercial pesticides. On the bright side, Bangladesh's thick forests provide teak. This is a wood used for shipbuilding and fine furniture.

1. What generalization could you make about living in Bangladesh?

    A. Living conditions there are very crowded.
    B. Windsurfing is a common sport there.
    C. It is a good place to eat seafood.
    D. There are wide open spaces and few people.

2. What generalization could you make about the economy of Bangladesh?

    A. It depends on fishing.
    B. It depends on shipbuilding.
    C. It depends on farming.
    D. None of the above.

3. What generalization could you make about its people?

    A. They are mostly Hindu.
    B. They are very poor.
    C. They are good swimmers.
    D. They are very healthy.

4. In general, which area of Bangladesh's economy holds the most promise?

    A. fishing industry
    B. forestry products
    C. water sports
    D. umbrella manufacturing

Map and Graph Skills Activity 5

Using a Map Scale

NATIONAL GEOGRAPHY STANDARDS 1 AND 3: The geographically informed person knows how to use maps and understands how to analyze the spatial organization of people, places, and environments on Earth's surface.

 ## Learning the Skill

Scale is used to represent size and distance on maps. For example, 1 inch on a map might represent 100 miles (161 kilometers) of distance on the earth's surface. A map scale is usually shown with a measuring line, called a scale bar, which can help you find distances on a map. To use the scale bar, follow these steps:

- Find the unit of measurement and the distance it represents.
- Measure the distance between two points using a ruler.
- Multiply that number by the miles or kilometers each unit represents.

Applying the Skill

Directions: The map at right shows South Asia. Study the map and use it to answer the questions on the next page in the spaces provided.

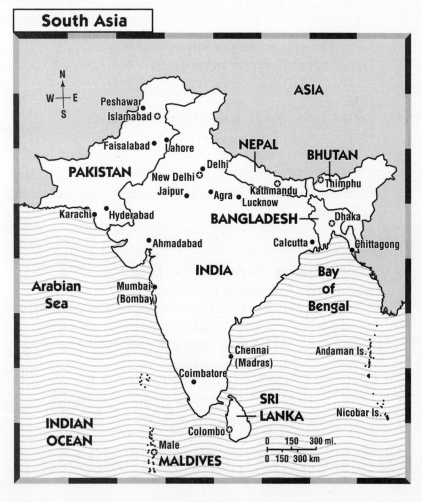

South Asia

N W E S

ASIA

Peshawar
Islamabad ⊛

Faisalabad • Lahore

NEPAL

BHUTAN

Delhi •
New Delhi ⊛
Jaipur • • Agra
Kathmandu ⊛ Thimphu

PAKISTAN

Lucknow

Karachi • Hyderabad

BANGLADESH

Dhaka ⊛

Ahmadabad

Calcutta •
Chittagong

INDIA

Bay of Bengal

Arabian Sea

Mumbai •
(Bombay)

Chennai
(Madras) •

Andaman Is.

Coimbatore •

SRI LANKA

Nicobar Is.

INDIAN OCEAN

Colombo ⊛
• Male
MALDIVES

0   150   300 mi.
0 150 300 km

SOUTH ASIA

Map and Graph Skills Activity 5 (continued)

1. What two units of measurement are used on this map scale?

2. About how far is it from Calcutta to Dhaka?

3. Which city is closest to New Delhi: Lucknow, Agra, or Jaipur?

4. About how far would you travel if you drove from the western border of Nepal to the eastern border?

5. Which city lies about 600 miles southwest of Jaipur?

6. Which city lies about 250 kilometers south of Islamabad?

7. **Critical Thinking** You want to travel from Kathmandu to Calcutta by train. The train moves at a pace of 50 miles per hour (80 kilometers per hour) and will make no stops along the way. About how long will your journey take? How did you arrive at your answer?

8. **Activity** You plan to make a hiking trip to South Asia but cannot decide on whether you should visit Bangladesh or Nepal. You have a firm goal of hiking at least 25 miles (40 kilometers) every day. Consult a physical map of South Asia to decide in which country you think you would be more likely to meet your goal. Then, on a separate sheet of paper, write a paragraph on your findings.

Practicing the Skill

Directions: Answer the following questions based on the map by circling the letter of the correct answer.

1. About how far is it from Male to Colombo?

   A. 150 miles (240 kilometers)
   B. 300 miles (480 kilometers)
   C. 450 miles (720 kilometers)
   D. 600 miles (960 kilometers)

2. Which of the following cities is farthest from Islamabad?

   A. Delhi
   B. Hyderabad
   C. Jaipur
   D. Agra

3. About how far is it from Calcutta to Ahmadabad?

   A. 600 miles (960 kilometers)
   B. 800 miles (1,280 kilometers)
   C. 975 miles (1,560 kilometers)
   D. 1,200 miles (1,920 kilometers)

Reading and Writing Skills Activity 5
Analyzing a Primary Source

CHAPTER 5

SOCIAL STUDIES OBJECTIVE: To analyze a primary source document.

 ## Learning the Skill

Historians figure out what happened in the past by combing through bits of evidence from the past to reconstruct events. These bits of historical evidence are called primary sources. Primary sources are records of events by the people who witnessed them. Examples of primary sources include letters, diaries, photographs, news articles, and legal documents. Use the following guidelines to help you analyze a primary source:

1. **Consider the Accuracy** Primary sources often give detailed accounts of events. These primary sources do not always give the most accurate account of an event. Often the creators do not anticipate that their work will be so important.

2. **Consider Perspective** The creators of primary sources look upon events with their own point of view. For example, when discussing the results of a presidential election, someone in the party whose candidate was elected would probably have a different point of view from someone in the party whose candidate was not elected. The creator of the primary source has one point of view, but other viewpoints probably exist. Make sure you take into account many viewpoints before drawing any conclusions about the past.

3. **Consider the Whole** As a child, you may have heard the story about the blind men who try to describe an elephant from their own perceptions. The blind man who touched the elephant's trunk thought that it was like a snake. The blind man who touched the elephant's tail thought it was like a rope. The blind man who touched the elephant's leg thought that it was like a tree. Each blind man was equally correct and equally wrong, because each only knew part of the elephant. As an historian, you may have to put together pieces of information that seem to make no sense at first. Try to consider the whole picture. One source may not have all the information.

Applying the Skill

Directions: Read the following passage from Mohandas Gandhi's autobiography. He is describing his attempt to travel from India to Great Britain. Then answer the questions in the space provided.

> With my mother's permission and blessings, I set off [excitedly] for Bombay, leaving my wife with a baby of a few months. But on arrival there friends told my brother that the Indian Ocean was rough in June and July, and as this was my first voyage, I should not be allowed to sail until November. Someone also reported that a steamer [ship] had just been sunk in a gale. This made my brother uneasy, and he refused to take the risk of allowing me to sail immediately. Leaving me with a friend in Bombay, he returned to Rajkot to resume his duty. He put the money for my travelling expenses in the keeping of a brother-in-law, and left word with some friends to give me whatever help I might need.

Excerpted from Mohandas K. Gandhi, *The Story of My Experiments with Truth—An Autobiography*. Retrieved August 17, 2001, from http://web.mahatma.org.in/

1. Who wrote this passage?

_____

2. What does the author describe?

_____

_____

3. What were the reasons that Gandhi could not sail immediately?

_____

_____

_____

_____

Directions: Find a primary source from your past—a photo, a report card, or an old newspaper clipping, for example. Bring this primary source to class and answer the following questions.

4. What is your primary source?

_____

5. Briefly explain what this primary source shows about the time from which it comes.

_____

_____

_____

Practicing the Skill

Directions: Answer the following questions by circling the letter of the correct answer.

1. What is a primary source?

    A. a record of an event by a person who witnessed it

    B. a biography

    C. a research report

    D. an historical fact

2. Which of the following would NOT be a primary source?

    A. a photo

    B. a letter

    C. a diary

    D. a fictional novel

GeoLab Activity 5

Mapping India's Physical Features

From the classroom of Mary D'Angelo, Boys Town High School, Omaha, Nebraska

Learn more about India's physical features. Use that information to create a map showcasing some of its landforms.

Background

India is a land of stark contrasts. Although India is still primarily rural and agricultural, cities such as Calcutta and Mumbai are growing. People who are seeking better lives move to these cities to find good jobs and decent housing. Where and how did these cities begin? Complete a map of India's physical features to gain a better idea of where the major Indian cities are located. Think about the impact the land's physical features may have had on the development of these cities.

Materials

- physical and political maps of India
- large sheet of sturdy poster board or cardboard
- uncooked macaroni noodles
- food coloring in several different colors
- pencil and paper
- small labels you make or purchase
- adhesive of some kind to apply labels
- white glue
- colored string

What to Do

1. Draw a freehand outline map of India. Sketch in the general areas of different elevations as shown on the reference physical map. Make a key that identifies each elevation level you have drawn.
2. Separate the macaroni noodles into a small pile for each elevation level you will show on your map. Use the food coloring and dye each level a different color.
3. Glue the macaroni noodles to your map according to your elevation key. Fill in all areas of India. Add colored string to represent major rivers.
4. Identify major mountain ranges, plateaus, and other features. Write the names on small labels and add them to your map.
5. Identify the location of the following cities on your map: New Delhi, Calcutta, Mumbai, Chennai, and Jaipur. Label these cities also.
6. As a class or group, discuss the physical features found near the cities. Make a list of these features. Discuss how these features influenced the location of the cities.

CHAPTER 5

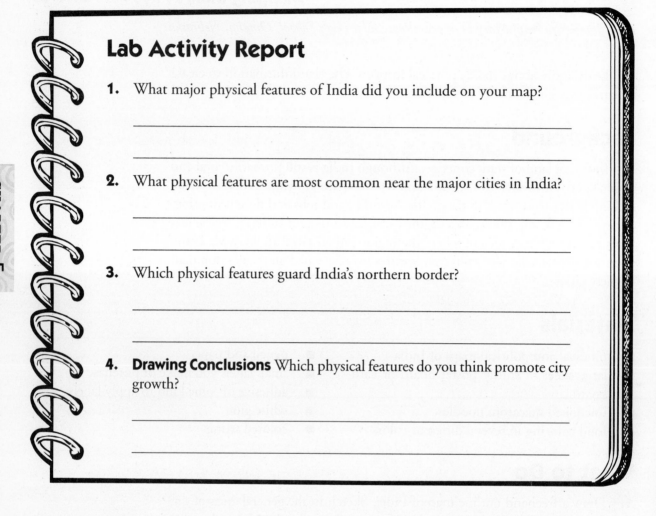

Lab Activity Report

1. What major physical features of India did you include on your map?

_____

_____

2. What physical features are most common near the major cities in India?

_____

_____

3. Which physical features guard India's northern border?

_____

_____

4. **Drawing Conclusions** Which physical features do you think promote city growth?

_____

_____

The citizens of the Kingdom of Bhutan, India's neighbor, recognize birthdays in an unusual way. All citizens officially become one year older on New Year's Day.

Go A Step Further

The Hindu faith is the primary religion in India and greatly influences the day-to-day living of the Indian people. Investigate library resources and/or the Internet to learn five facts about Hinduism you did not know from reading your textbook. Share your findings with the class.

CHAPTER 5

Enrichment Activity 5

The Himalaya—The World's Highest Mountains

Directions: Read the following article about the Himalaya. Then fill in the flow-chart below and answer the questions in the space provided.

The Himalaya are the highest mountain range in the world. Many of their snowcapped peaks rise more than 5 miles (8 km). In fact *Himalaya* means the "home of snow" in the ancient Indian language of Sanskrit. The most famous Himalayan peak is Mount Everest. It is the world's tallest mountain, soaring to more than 29,000 feet (8,839 m).

Together with the Karakoram Range, the Himalaya stretch 1,500 miles (2,414 km) from east to west. These two ranges form the northern border of the Indian subcontinent. The Ganges, India's largest river, begins in the Himalaya.

The Himalaya are the result of a massive collision between two continents. India was not always a part of Asia. Originally it was the northern tip of the Indo-Australian tectonic plate. India separated from the plate. Over tens of millions of years, India drifted northward. Finally, it collided with Asia. The edges of the huge landmasses crumpled. The earth's crust was pushed up, forming the Himalaya.

Many earthquakes and tremors shake the Himalaya each year. These tremors show that the mountains are still in motion. As they constantly shift, the Himalaya rise even higher.

Taking Another Look

1. What happened as India drifted northward?

_____

_____

2. What happens as the mountains continue to shift?

_____

_____

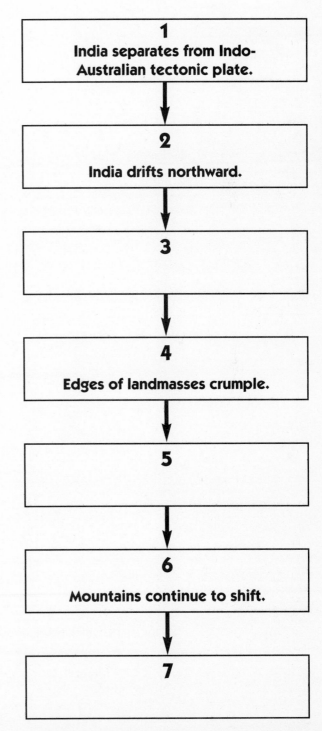

1 India separates from Indo-Australian tectonic plate.

2 India drifts northward.

3

4 Edges of landmasses crumple.

5

6 Mountains continue to shift.

7

Chapter 5, Section Resources

SECTIONS

Guided Reading Activity 5-1

India

DIRECTIONS: Answering Questions Reading the section and answering the questions below will help you learn more about the country of India. Use your textbook to fill in the blanks.

1. What is a subcontinent?

_____

2. What forms India's northern border?

_____

3. Describe the climate of India.

_____

4. What is important to India's economy?

_____

5. What is a cottage industry?

_____

6. What are environmental challenges that India faces?

_____

7. Where were the first Indian civilizations located?

_____

8. Who led the Indian independence movement? What was the strategy?

_____

_____

9. What is the main religion, and how does it affect life?

_____

10. Where do most of the people live?

_____

_____

Guided Reading Activity 5-2

Other Countries of South Asia

DIRECTIONS: Filling in the Blanks Reading the section and completing the sentences below will help you learn more about the countries of South Asia. Refer to your textbook to fill in the blanks.

Pakistan and Bangladesh are largely **(1)** _____. Although they

share the same religion, they have different **(2)** _____ and languages.

Pakistan and India both want Kashmir for its **(3)** _____

_____. The major languages in Pakistan are **(4)** _____

and **(5)** _____. About 70 percent of Pakistan's people live in

(6) _____ _____.

Bangladesh is nearly surrounded by **(7)** _____. There are two

major rivers—the **(8)** _____ and the **(9)** _____.

Most people earn a living by **(10)** _____. Bangladesh is one of the

most **(11)** _____ populated countries and one of the world's

(12) _____ countries.

Nepal's land is dominated by the **(13)** _____, the world's

highest mountain range. Nepal's economy depends on **(14)** _____.

Most people in Nepal are related to peoples in northern **(15)** _____

and Tibet.

The major landform of Bhutan are the **(16)** _____. Most of

Bhutan's people are **(17)** _____ _____. Most people

in Bhutan speak the **(18)** _____ dialect.

Sri Lanka has good fertile soil for **(19)** _____. Sri Lanka is one

of the world's leading producers of **(20)** _____ and rubber. Sri Lankans

belong to two major ethnic groups: the **(21)** _____ and the Tamils.

Chapter 6 Resources

CHAPTER 6

CHINA AND ITS NEIGHBORS

Vocabulary Activity 6

DIRECTIONS: Word Puzzle Fill in the puzzle by spelling out the terms called for in the 12 clues. Then complete term 13, spelled vertically, and write its definition on line 13.

high-technology industries
consumer goods
fault
calligraphy
communist state

nomad
dike
typhoon

dynasty
pagoda
empire
yurt
invest

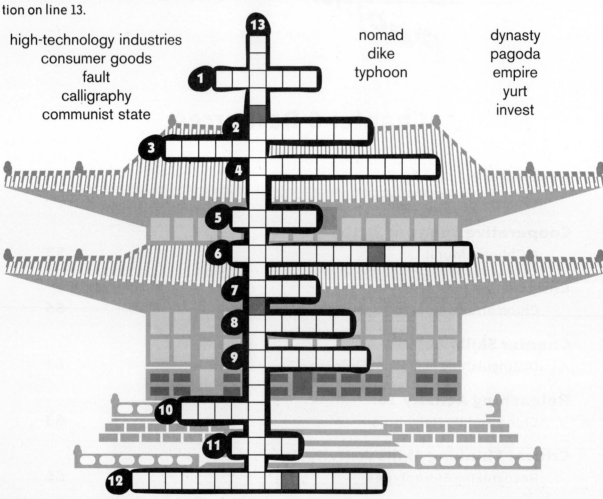

1. a many-storied, traditional Buddhist tower

2. a tropical storm with high winds and heavy rain, like an Atlantic hurricane

3. a group of territories under one ruler

4. the art of beautiful writing, as practiced in China

5. a person who moves from place to place with herds of animals

6. products people use, such as cars, televisions, clothes, motorcycles

7. a round tent of animal skin used by nomadic herders

8. to put money into something for a later profit

9. a line of rulers from a single family

10. crack in the earth's crust

11. a high bank of soil to prevent a river from overflowing

12. a country in which the government has strong control over the economy and society

13. _____

_____

Cooperative Learning Activity 6

A Chinese Mural

Background

With nearly 1.3 billion people, China has the largest population in the world. One of every five people in the world lives in China. About three of every four Chinese workers are farmers who live in the countryside. Because the population of the country is so large, China also has 7 of the 75 largest cities in the world. You can understand more about how China's large population affects the people who live there by making a "mural banner."

Group Directions

1. Use Chapter 6 and library resources or the Internet to learn about life and culture in China. Think about the effect China's large population has on the culture.

2. Using books, magazines, or the Internet, find pictures that show scenes from daily life in Chinese cities and in the countryside.

3. Use what you learn to sketch scenes showing life and culture in China today.

4. Think about these elements of China, and any others you find during your research, to inspire your artwork:

landscape	architecture and art
ceremonies	work and play activities
clothing style	modes of transportation

Organizing the Group

1. **Decision Making** As a class, decide on a uniform length of shelf or butcher paper that each group will use for its mural banner. Using the suggestions listed in the box above—and any ideas of your own—decide which characteristics of China your group will research.

2. **Individual Work** Do research to learn more about life and culture in China. Make sketches showing the people and land.

3. **Group Work** Share your sketches with your group. Together, plan the overall organization of the mural and decide the location of individual sketches within the mural.

CHAPTER 6

CHINA AND ITS NEIGHBORS

Cooperative Learning Activity 6 (continued)

4. **Additional Group Work** As a group, unroll your paper and make a color-ful mural banner. You might use different colored markers, crayons, or watercolor paints for your mural.

5. **Group Sharing** Hang your mural banner on a classroom wall, along with the banners of other groups. The arrangement will make a giant wall mural that reflects daily life and culture in different parts of China. Invite other classes, teachers, and interested adults to view your class artwork.

Group Process Questions

- What is the most important thing you learned about Chinese life and cul-ture from this activity?

- What part of the project did you enjoy most?

- What problems did you have?

- How did you solve the problems?

- Was it easy to agree on the organization of your group mural banner? Why or why not?

Quick Check

1. Was the goal of the assignment clear at all times?

_____

_____

_____

2. Did each group member contribute equally to the mural?

_____

_____

_____

3. Were you satisfied with your work on this project? Why or why not?

_____

_____

_____

Chapter Map Activity 6

Teaching Strategy

China is the third-largest country in the world. The arts and ideas of ancient times still influence the country, even though China has been experiencing rapid change in recent years as it strives to modernize its economy. Throughout their history, the people of Mongolia and Taiwan have been closely tied to their powerful neighbor.

Regional and Political Maps

Place Location Activity

Reproduce the regional map for each student. Ask students to:

- Label the following places and their boundaries: China, Taiwan, Mongolia.
- Trace the following rivers: Brahmaputra, Tarim, Liao, Songhua, Yellow, Yangtze, Mekong, Salween, Xi, Amur.
- Label the following bodies of water: Sea of Japan, Yellow Sea, East China Sea, South China Sea, Taiwan Strait.
- With an arrow, indicate on your map in what direction the United States is from this region.

Reproduce the political map for each student. Ask students to:

- Label the countries and bodies of water. *(See the list of countries and bodies of water for the regional map.)*
- Mark and label the national capital and major cities of each country. *(Remind students to include a map key.)*

Discussing the Maps

1. In which direction would you travel if you journeyed in a straight line from Mongolia's capital to China's capital? What is the approximate straight-line distance between the two cities? *(You would travel southeast to journey from Ulaanbaatar, Mongolia, to Beijing, China. The two cities are about 680 miles [1,088 km] apart.)*
2. True or false: Hong Kong is an independent nation. *(False; since 1997, Hong Kong has been a part of China.)*
3. Taiwan lies about how far from the Chinese mainland? *(about 100 miles [160 km])*
4. Name the body of water that separates mainland China from Taiwan. *(The Taiwan Strait separates them.)*

APPLYING GEOGRAPHY SKILLS
Mapping Walls and Canals

You may use the following activity as a portfolio or extra credit project.

Ask students to use the library or Internet to find the locations of the following: Great Wall of China, Wall of

Genghis Khan, and the Grand Canal. Then have students use copies of their completed political maps to trace the paths of these three creations. Students should use distinctive symbols to designate each, and should include a map key.

Physical and Capitals and Major Cities Maps

Place Location Activity

Reproduce the physical map for each student. Ask students to:

- Label the countries, rivers, and bodies of water. *(See the list of countries, rivers, and bodies of water for the regional map.)*
- Mark and label the major cities of each country. *(Remind students to include a map key.)*
- Label the following: Manchurian Plain, Gobi, Altay Mountains, Tian Shan, Taklimakan Desert, Qilian Shan, Kunlun Shan, Plateau of Tibet, Liaodong Peninsula, Shandong Peninsula, North China Plain, Leizhou Peninsula, Hainan, Himalaya.

Reproduce the capitals and major cities map for each student. Ask students to:

- Label the countries. *(See the list of countries for the regional map.)*
- Label the capital and major cities of each country.

Discussing the Maps

1. Name the source and destination of the Yangtze River. *(The Yangtze River begins in the Plateau of Tibet and empties into the East China Sea.)*
2. True or false: The Tropic of Cancer passes through Taiwan. *(true)*
3. Why do you suppose the population density of eastern China is so much greater than that of western China? *(Western China is covered by plateaus and rugged mountains. Most of the region is not good for farming, and living conditions there are very difficult.)*
4. What climate do you think is found in the Plateau of Tibet? *(The Plateau of Tibet has a high latitude/highland climate, with cool summers and extremely cold winters.)*

CHAPTER 6

CHINA AND ITS NEIGHBORS

Chapter Map Activity 6

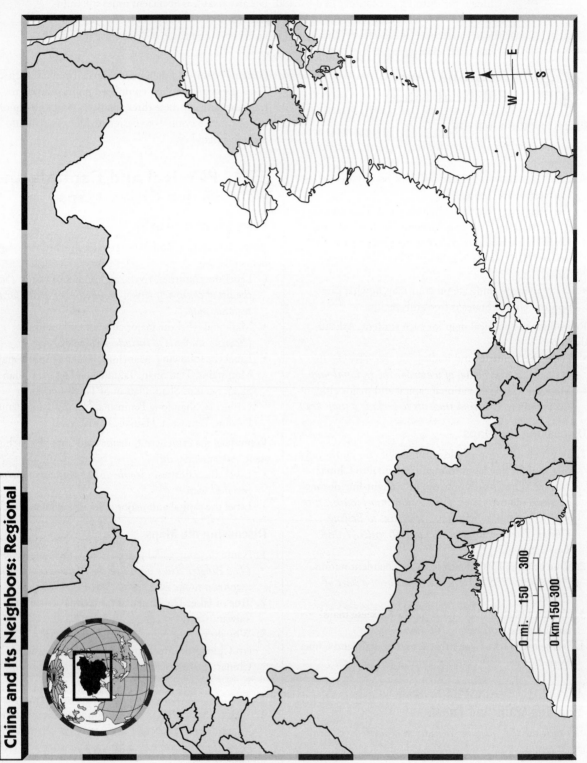

China and Its Neighbors: Regional

0 mi.   150   300

0 km 150 300

Chapter Map Activity 6

CHAPTER 6

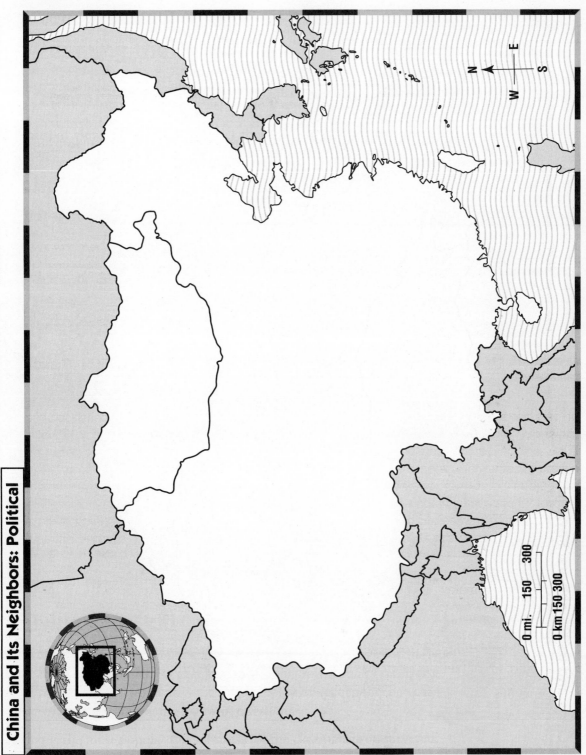

China and Its Neighbors: Political

0 mi. 150 300

0 km 150 300

57

Chapter Map Activity 6

CHAPTER 6

China and Its Neighbors: Physical

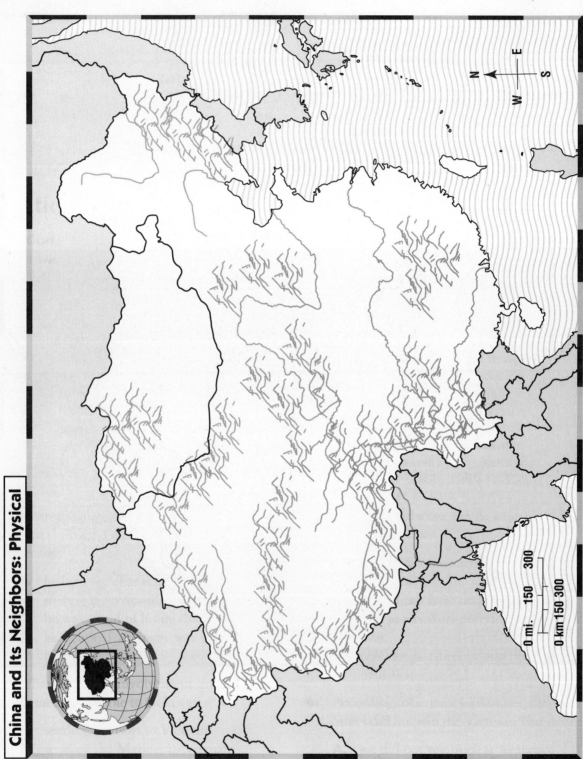

0 mi. 150 300

0 km 150 300

Chapter Map Activity 6

China and Its Neighbors: Capitals and Major Cities

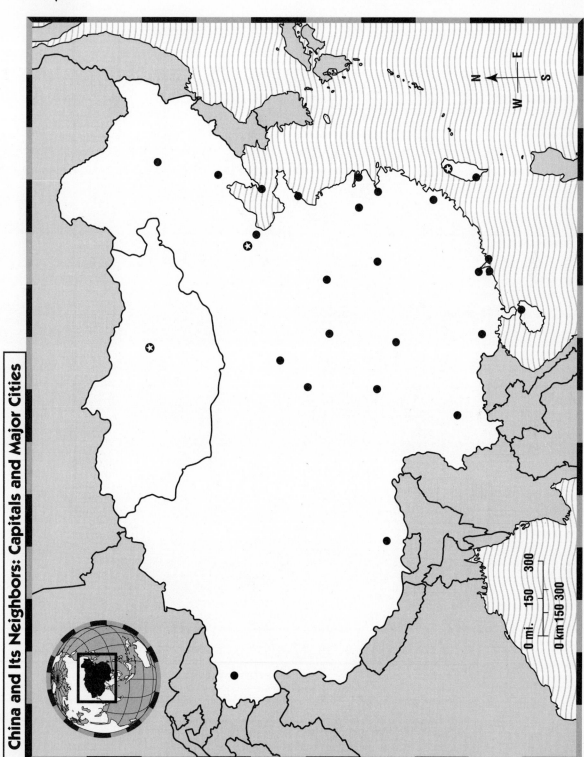

Name _____ Date _____ Class _____

Chapter Skills Activity 6

Distinguishing Fact From Opinion

 ## Learning the Skill

Facts can be proved by evidence such as records, documents, or historical sources. *Opinions* are based on people's differing values and beliefs. To help you identify facts and opinions, read or listen to the information carefully. Identify the facts. If a statement can be proved, it is factual. Check the sources for the facts. Identify opinions by looking for statements of feelings or beliefs.

Practicing the Skill

Directions: Read the passage below, then answer the questions that follow in the spaces provided or on a separate sheet of paper.

> Only people who live under democracy truly appreciate and cherish the merits of democracy. Whether China likes it or not, Taiwan has developed into such a true democracy.
>
> By freely and democratically electing a new president last March 18, the people of Taiwan have demonstrated that the will of the people of Taiwan cannot be coerced [forced]. The right of self-determination of Taiwan's people cannot be sabotaged [harmed].
>
> The new American president indeed will need a new China policy. A new U.S. China policy needs to be clear and must reflect the reality of the Taiwan Strait—that the People's Republic is the People's Republic and that Taiwan is Taiwan. Indeed, the U.S. "One China Policy" needs to be replaced by a "One China, One Taiwan Policy," a policy that reflects reality.

Source: Ho, Iris. "U.S. China Policy." *The International Herald Tribune.* (November 24, 2000). Retrieved December 10, 2000 from the World Wide Web: www.iht.com/articles/2315.htm

1. List the facts stated in the passage. _____

2. List the opinions from the passage. _____

3. What is the purpose of this passage? _____

Applying the Skill

Directions: Read an editorial in your local newspaper, then answer the following questions on a separate sheet of paper.

1. List the facts stated in the editorial.
2. List the opinions from the editorial.
3. What is the purpose of this editorial?

Reteaching Activity 6

China has the third-largest land area of any country in the world. Its vast landscape includes huge mountains, large deserts, and mighty rivers. About 1.25 billion people, one-fifth of the world's population, live in China. Taiwan is an island to the east of China, and Mongolia borders China on the north. Throughout history, Taiwan and Mongolia have had close ties with their much larger neighbor.

DIRECTIONS: Making a Chart Read each word or phrase below. Each item applies to China or to either or both Taiwan and Mongolia. Write each letter in the appropriate box.

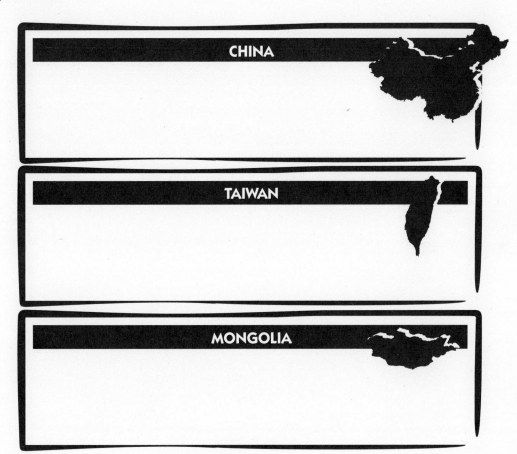

CHINA

TAIWAN

MONGOLIA

A. Ulaanbaatar

B. Hong Kong

C. Plateau of Tibet

D. High technology industries

E. Nomads

F. Communist

G. Great Wall of China

H. Taipei

I. Land of the Blue Sky

J. Turpan Depression

K. sugarcane and fruit

L. Naadam Festival

M. Tiananmen Square

N. Porcelain

O. democracy

Critical Thinking Skills Activity 6
Recognizing Stereotypes

SOCIAL STUDIES OBJECTIVE: Detect bias and analyze propaganda.

 ## Learning the Skill

A **stereotype** is a fixed mental picture of the way members of a group think or behave. Assigning simple or general characteristics to all members of a group of people creates stereotypes. The group could be a country, a religion, a race, an age group, and so on. When you stereotype, you tend to ignore individual traits or characteristics. For example, the stereotype of young people as rebellious, self-centered, careless, and in love with loud music clearly does not include all young people. Another example is the stereotype of the "ugly American." This stereotype assumes that all Americans are rich, proud, demanding, and rude. Stereotypes are oversimplified opinions that do not recognize that individual people have special qualities of their own. To recognize stereotypes, follow these steps:

• Look at the information and find general statements about groups of people. Try to notice exaggerations, often indicated by words like *all*, *none*, *always*, and *never*. Identify strong adjectives such as *lazy*, *sneaky*, *cruel*, or *corrupt*. Note a positive or negative tone to the description.

• Once you recognize a stereotype, evaluate its accuracy. Ask yourself, "Is this statement or image true for all the members of that group?" Think about whether the stereotype puts a positive or negative slant on the information concerning a specific group.

Applying the Skill

Directions:
A. Put a check mark in front of each statement below that represents a stereotype, then answer the question that follows.

_____ **1.** Chinese civilization is more than 4,000 years old.

_____ **2.** About 30 percent of the population of China live in cities.

_____ **3.** The Chinese are excellent gymnasts and musicians.

_____ **4.** Chinese students work and study much harder than American students.

_____ **5.** Taiwanese people excel at computers and understanding new technology.

_____ **6.** Poor people in Hong Kong live on boats, called "junks," in the harbors.

_____ **7.** Mongolians are famous for their skills in raising and riding horses.

_____ **8.** Mongolia is more than twice the size of Texas.

_____ **9.** Chinese are great cooks and own successful restaurants.

_____ **10.** Chinese children are always well behaved and respectful of their elders.

What stereotypes exist about groups in your community? Evaluate their accuracy.

_____

_____

_____

CHINA AND ITS NEIGHBORS

Critical Thinking Skills Activity 6 (continued)

B. Think of a television program or movie you have seen, or a book you have read, that was set in China or a "Chinatown" in a major United States city. Did the characters seem stereotyped? Answer the following questions.

1. What was the name of the television program, movie, or book?

_____

_____

_____

2. What was it about?

_____

_____

_____

_____

_____

_____

3. Describe the character or characters that seemed stereotyped. In what way did the character fit a popular stereotype of Chinese people?

_____

_____

_____

_____

_____

_____

_____

Practicing the Skill

Directions: Answer the following questions by circling the letter of each correct answer.

1. Which of the following statements about stereotypes is NOT true?

   A. Stereotypes are general statements about a group of people.

   B. Stereotypes can be made about any group of people.

   C. Stereotypes recognize the individual qualities of the people who make up the group.

   D. Stereotypes are fixed mental pictures of how certain people think or behave.

2. Which of the following groups can be stereotyped?

   A. senior citizens

   B. Asians

   C. Buddhists

   D. all of the above

3. Which of the following statements is a stereotype?

   A. Workers in Taiwan produce many useful products such as clothing, radios, and computers.

   B. The Chinese are famous for their silk drawings, painting, sculpture, and architecture.

   C. Chinese are much more quiet and polite than Americans.

   D. Mongolians have a higher rate of literacy than the Chinese.

Name _____ Date _____ Class _____

Map and Graph Skills Activity 6

Comparing Two or More Graphs

NATIONAL GEOGRAPHY STANDARD 15: The geographically informed person knows and understands how physical systems affect human systems.

 ## Learning the Skill

Comparing graphs gives you a better understanding of a topic. When comparing graphs, first see how the graphs are related. Are they the same kind of graph? Do they address the same topic? Do they use the same type of measurement? Then look for similarities and differences in the information presented in the graphs. To compare graphs, follow these steps:

- Read the title and labels on each graph to see how they are related.
- Look for similarities and differences in the information given on each graph.
- Draw conclusions based on the comparison.

Applying the Skill

Directions: The circle graphs below give you information about China's economy. The graphs show the percentage of workers in each part of the Chinese economy and the percentage of the country's goods and services they produce. (China has a workforce of about 700 million people.) Study the graphs and use them to answer the questions on the next page in the spaces provided.

China's Economy

Goods and Services Produced in China

Industry 35%

Services 50%

Agriculture 15%

Key
- Agriculture
- Industry
- Services

Workers' Jobs in China

Agriculture 50%

Industry 24%

Services 26%

CHINA AND ITS NEIGHBORS

Map and Graph Skills Activity 6 (continued)

1. How do the largest percentage of Chinese workers make a living?

   _____

2. What makes up the largest percentage of China's economy, and about what percentage of workers have jobs there?

   _____

   _____

3. What is the smallest segment of the Chinese economy?

   _____

4. True or False: The total number of Chinese working in industry and services is greater than the total number of Chinese working in agriculture.

   _____

5. **Critical Thinking** Look at the percentage of Chinese workers in agriculture and compare it to the percentage of agricultural goods produced in China. What do you see? Are you surprised by the different percentages? Why or why not?

   _____

   _____

   _____

   _____

6. **Critical Thinking** Study a physical map of China, then speculate on where most agricultural activity in the country probably takes place. Why do you think it takes place there?

   _____

   _____

   _____

7. **Activity** On a separate sheet of paper, write a paragraph to describe the relationship between the percentage of workers in each part of China's economy and the total goods and services they produce.

Practicing the Skill

Directions: Answer the following questions based on the graphs by circling the letter of the correct answer.

1. The percentage of Chinese who work in industry is

   A. about the same as the percentage who work in agriculture.
   B. much greater than the percentage who work in agriculture.
   C. about the same as the percentage who work in services.
   D. much greater than the percentage who work in services.

2. In China, the services segment of the economy is

   A. smaller than the industrial segment of the economy.
   B. larger than the agricultural segment of the economy.
   C. the smallest segment of the economy.
   D. smaller than the agricultural segment, but larger than the industrial segment.

3. Chinese farmers

   A. make up the smallest part of the Chinese workforce.
   B. make up the second-largest part of the Chinese workforce.
   C. produce more goods and services than any other workers in the country.
   D. produce fewer goods and services than any other workers in the country.

Reading and Writing Skills Activity 6
Analyzing Secondary Sources

SOCIAL STUDIES OBJECTIVE: Analyze information contained in secondary sources.

Learning the Skill

Secondary sources use information gathered from others. They tell about an event, but the writers did not participate in the event. Newspaper articles, textbooks, and biographies are examples of secondary sources. To analyze the information contained in a secondary source, use the following steps.

1. Identify the author of the document.
2. Determine when and where the document was written.
3. Read the document for its content.
4. Identify the author's opinions, bias, and point of view.
5. Decide what kind of information the document provides and what is missing.

Applying the Skill

Directions: In 1989 university students in China led protests and demonstrations in Tiananmen Square. The protests began when Hu Yaobang died. He had been removed from leadership in the Communist Party because he wanted to allow more freedom in China. Read the sources and answer the questions that follow.

> On April 15, 1989, Hu Yaobang died of a heart attack. Students in Beijing. . . seized the opportunity to stage demonstrations in his honor, demanding that the verdict against him be reversed but also demanding other reforms. University students were particularly eager for such an excuse that week; only two days before Hu's death, the government had revoked [canceled] a previous declaration that university graduates would be permitted to search for jobs where they wished, instead of being assigned jobs by the state. Thousands of students demonstrated in Tiananmen Square on April 17, and more demonstrations followed.

Moise, Edwin E. *Modern China: A History*, 2nd ed. (London: Longman House), 1994: 217.

> In April 1989, when Hu Yaobang's death became known, students all over China discussed Chinese problems: the corruption of party officials and the slow progress of democracy which Hu Yaobang was associated with. Corruption in government circles had long been a problem. . . .
> One of the fundamental principles of democracy has always been the right to peaceful demonstration. The assembly of Beijing students decided to put this to the test by marching out of their campuses and assembling in Tiananmen Square in central Beijing to express their grief over Hu's death. This demonstration was not dispersed [broken up] by the security police.

Bradley, John. *China: A New Revolution?* (New York: Aladdin Books), 1990: 24.

CHINA AND ITS NEIGHBORS
Reading and Writing Skills Activity 6 (continued)

1. What is the general topic of the two secondary sources?

_____

_____

2. When was each document written?

_____

_____

3. What information does each document provide?

_____

_____

_____

_____

4. What differences do you note between these passages?

_____

_____

_____

_____

Practicing the Skill

Directions: Answer the following questions by circling the letter of the correct answer.

1. Which of the following is a secondary source?
   A. a letter   **C.** a photo
   B. a diary   **D.** a biography

2. Which of the following best describes a secondary source?
   A. The writer experienced the event.
   B. The writer interviewed someone who participated in the event.
   C. The writer states the facts of the event without expressing an opinion.
   D. The writer saw the event, but waited until later to write down what occurred.

GeoLab Activity 6

Chinese Cooking

From the classroom of Don Mendenhall, Coleman Junior School, Van Buren, Arkansas

Discover some of the foods the Chinese people enjoy. Gather ingredients they would use in cooking, and then prepare a dish typical of this region of the world.

Background

China is the most heavily populated country in the world. One of this country's most difficult tasks is to provide enough food for its people. The Chinese must select food and prepare it to use available ingredients and other resources in the best possible way. As you cook the following Chinese dish, you will more easily see how the Chinese way of cooking creates conservation of time and energy and produces virtually no waste.

Materials

- wok, electric or stovetop
- wooden spoon
- serving platter
- forks
- 1 package boil-in-the-bag white rice
- 3 tablespoons of peanut oil
- 3 green onions
- 1 yellow bell pepper
- 5 celery stalks
- 1/2 pound of snow peas
- 8 ounces of mushrooms
- one 8-ounce can of bamboo shoots
- one 8-ounce can of water chestnuts
- 1 pound of chow mein noodles
- 1-quart saucepan
- chopping knife and cutting board
- plates or bowls
- 2 cups of water
- 1 yellow onion
- 1 red bell pepper
- 1 green bell pepper
- 3 carrots
- 8 ounces of bean sprouts
- 1 head of broccoli
- soy sauce (optional)

What to Do

Note to the Teacher:

To save time and avoid any accidents, you may wish to precut the vegetables before class. Also, you may wish to enlist additional adult help to supervise around the cooking stove.

1. Carefully chop all the vegetables into small pieces.
2. Heat the water in the saucepan and heat the oil in the wok at the same time.
3. When the water boils, put the bag of rice into the saucepan. Cook according to directions on the package.

CHAPTER 6

4. When the oil is hot, place the chopped yellow onions in the wok and cook until they appear clear. Stir frequently.

5. Place all the remaining vegetables in the wok, stirring constantly. Cook for about 5 minutes until tender but not limp.

6. When the rice is done, pour it onto the large serving dish. Then place the cooked vegetables over the rice. Top the dish with the chow mein noodles. Use soy sauce to season as desired.

7. Eat and enjoy!

Lab Activity Report

1. How does cutting the vegetables into small pieces conserve energy?

_____

2. What vegetable seemed to take the longest to cook?

_____

_____

3. In wok cooking, why it is important to have all the ingredients prepared before the cooking begins?

_____

_____

4. Drawing Conclusions Why do you think the Chinese eat so many vegetables?

_____

_____

The Chinese use a bright red berry called a Chinese wolfberry as a tonic in traditional Chinese medicine. This fruit, also known as the "matrimony vine," is used to cool the blood, reduce fevers, prevent nosebleeds, improve absorption of nutrients, increase functioning of the kidneys and liver, and to restore blurred vision.

Enrichment Activity 6

Chinese Ink Painting

CHAPTER 6

Directions: Read the following information about Chinese ink painting. Then answer the questions that follow on a separate sheet of paper.

Chinese ink painting is an ancient art that has been passed from teacher to student for more than 2,000 years. Chinese artists use specially made ink for their paintings. You may think of ink as the liquid that flows from pens. Chinese painters use ink that starts as a solid stick. To make the ink, wood from pine trees is burned in a special room with silk strips hanging from the ceiling. As the wood burns, soot collects on the silk. The soot is carefully scraped from the silk strips. It is heated and strained to create a fine powder. The powder is mixed with glue and poured into molds. The ink makers place the molds in rooms built of sandalwood. The ink hardens in the molds. As it hardens, the scent from the sandalwood and the pine join together. Later, when the artist mixes the ink stick with water, there is a pleasant smell from the ink. The shade of the ink depends on the part of the pine tree that is burned. The blackest ink comes from burning the center of a pine tree.

Before an artist begins a painting, he or she liquifies the ink in an inkstone. An inkstone has two sections: the grinding area and the well. The artist pours a small amount of pure water in the well and dips the end of the ink stick into it. The artist slowly and carefully rotates the moistened ink stick in the grinding area. The moistened ink runs from the grinding area into the well. There it mixes with the water. The water will darken and thicken to become ink. The artist will rotate the stick about 400 times to create two teaspoons of ink. The better the quality of the ink stick, the fewer the rotations that are needed to create the ink. The artist plans for the amount of ink needed to complete a painting. All the ink needed for the painting will be created at one time. Once in liquid form, it can be stored for several days in a covered container.

The artist uses brushes made of bamboo and different kinds of hairs. Some ancient brushes were made using mouse whiskers. Today brushes usually are made of rabbit's hair or sheep's wool.

Most Chinese ink painting is done on rice paper or silk. The Chinese invented paper in A.D. 105. The earliest paper was made by hand, using vegetable fibers matted together. Chinese ink painters still use handmade paper. The term "rice paper" refers to the technique of making paper by hand, not to the material used. Although rice and parts of a plant known as the rice-paper tree are used to make paper, it may also be made of linen, bamboo, or the bark of various trees. The artist selects the texture of paper that will work best with the subject of his or her painting. The paper, the ink, and the artist's touch work in harmony to create the beautiful landscapes common to Chinese ink painting.

Taking Another Look

1. What materials are used to make an ink stick?
2. How is the inkstone used to create the liquid ink?
3. What other materials are needed for a Chinese ink painting?
4. **Analyzing Information** A good quality ink stick is one of the most valuable gifts you can give to a Chinese artist. Why do you think this is so?

Chapter 6, Section Resources

SECTIONS

CHINA AND ITS NEIGHBORS

Guided Reading Activity 6-1

China's Land and Economy

DIRECTIONS: Reading for Accuracy Reading the section and completing the activity below will help you learn more about China's land and economy. Refer to your textbook to decide if a statement is true or false. Write **T** or **F**, and if a statement is false, rewrite it correctly.

_____ **1.** Mountains cover about one-third of China.

_____

_____ **2.** The rest of China is very fertile and full of grasslands.

_____

_____ **3.** The Yellow River valley is a very important farming area.

_____

_____ **4.** The Yellow River brought much devastation from flooding until dams and dikes were built.

_____

_____ **5.** The only natural dangers the Chinese face are earthquakes.

_____

_____ **6.** Individuals and businesses control the economy in China.

_____

_____ **7.** The Chinese government has allowed many features of the free enterprise system in order to make the economy stronger.

_____

_____ **8.** China's economic growth has led to major improvements in the nation's environment.

_____

_____ **9.** Hong Kong and Macau are centers of manufacturing, trade, and finance.

_____

SECTION 6-1

Guided Reading Activity 6-2

China's People and Culture

DIRECTIONS: Filling in the Blanks Reading the section and completing the sentences below will help you learn more about China's people and culture. Refer to your textbook to fill in the blanks.

China's population makes up about **(1)** _____-

_____ of all of the people in the world. Most belong to the ethnic

group called **(2)** _____ _____. As China's civilization

developed, they wanted to keep out **(3)** _____ _____.

To defend the northern area, they built the **(4)** _____

_____ _____ _____.

A Chinese thinker named **(5)** _____ said people should be

polite, **(6)** _____, **(7)** _____, and wise. Another

thinker named **(8)** _____ believed people should live simply; his ideas

were called **(9)** _____.

Foreign influences entered China during the **(10)** _____ and

(11) _____. Europeans wanted to open China to

(12) _____. After they overthrew the emperor, China became a

(13) _____. In **(14)** _____ Communists came into

power. In 1976 a new leader, **(15)** _____ _____,

wanted to make China a more open country. Critics claim Chinese leaders have no

respect for **(16)** _____ _____. China took control of

(17) _____ in 1950.

Most of China's people live in **(18)** _____ areas. Many

villages have **(19)** _____ _____. China's

(20) _____ are growing rapidly.

SECTION 6-2

77

CHINA AND ITS NEIGHBORS

Guided Reading Activity 6-3

China's Neighbors

DIRECTIONS: Outlining Reading the section and completing the outline below will help you learn more about China's neighbors. Refer to your textbook to fill in the blanks.

I. Taiwan

    A. Taiwan is an _____ country.

        1. It has a ridge of steep _____ through its center.

        2. The majority of the people live on the flat, fertile _____.

        3. Taiwan has _____ winters and hot, rainy summers.

    B. Taiwan has a very _____ economy.

        1. Its wealth comes from _____-_____ industries.

        2. It has a growing economic influence on its _____

            _____.

    C. _____ also contributes to the booming economy.

    D. Taiwan was once part of _____ empire.

        1. Then _____ took over the island.

        2. Then rule returned to _____ after World War II.

        3. In 1949 the _____ arrived in Taiwan.

        4. Today the government is a _____.

II. Mongolia

    A. Mongolia is a _____ country.

        1. Rugged _____ and high _____ rise in the west and center.

        2. The _____ landscape of the Gobi stretches over the southeast.

        3. The rest of the country is covered by _____.

    B. Mongolia is known as the Land of the _____ _____.

    C. Most of the people were _____.

    D. _____ _____ led Mongols on a series of conquests in the 1200s.

        1. The Mongols had the largest _____ _____ in history.

        2. It fell apart during the _____.

    E. Mongolia's main religion is _____.

SECTION 6-3

Chapter 7 Resources

CHAPTER 7

JAPAN AND THE KOREAS

Vocabulary Activity 7

DIRECTIONS: Fill in the Blanks Select a term to fill each blank in the paragraphs below.

archipelago

tsunami

intensive cultivation

clan

samurai

shogun

megalopolis

constitutional monarchy

monsoon

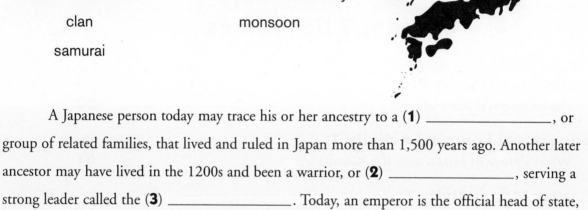

A Japanese person today may trace his or her ancestry to a (**1**) _____, or group of related families, that lived and ruled in Japan more than 1,500 years ago. Another later ancestor may have lived in the 1200s and been a warrior, or (**2**) _____, serving a strong leader called the (**3**) _____. Today, an emperor is the official head of state, but elected officials run the government. This form of democracy is known as a (**4**) _____.

When an earthquake occurs in the Pacific Ocean, it may create a huge sea wave called a (**5**) _____. This wave is especially dangerous to people who live near coasts, on isolated islands, or on a chain of islands, which is called an (**6**) _____.

If you lived in Japan today, you might live in a (**7**) _____, or the huge urban area that includes the capital city of Tokyo, as well as the cities of Yokohama, Osaka, and Nagoya. The Japanese, with little land, practice (**8**) _____, using every bit of land to grow crops.

Although North and South Korea are different countries, they share many similarities. For example, (**9**) _____ season affects the climate of both countries. Also, minerals are important resources in the Koreas.

Cooperative Learning Activity 7
What's New in Japan and the Koreas

Background

Japan, North Korea, and South Korea have been the source of news headlines throughout recent history. Business news has often focused on the latest Japanese products, including many that Americans enjoy, from computers to cars. The divided country of Korea sometimes makes headlines over disputes between the communist North and the democratic South. You will learn more about life in these countries today by following stories about them in the news.

Group Directions

1. Find news stories about Japan, North Korea, and South Korea to create your own television news broadcast.

2. Read articles in newspapers, newsmagazines, or online news sources for one week. Copy or download articles about Japan, North Korea, and South Korea. Research any background information that you will need.

3. Share the news and feature articles that you collect.

4. Plan the news broadcast. As with any news program, balance the positive and negative stories you will present. Consider dividing your program into segments such as the following:

late-breaking news	cultural reports
business	feature stories
weather	sports

Organizing the Group

1. **Decision Making** As a group, decide how to divide up the work. Decide who will be the news anchor, the sports anchor, and the weather reporter. Choose the group members who will do cultural features or any other segments you decide to do.

2. **Group Work/Decision Making** Review the news and feature articles found by group members. Choose the articles to go into the broadcast. Be sure to include something about each of the three countries—Japan, North Korea, and South Korea. Divide the articles among group members.

JAPAN AND THE KOREAS
Cooperative Learning Activity 7 (continued)

3. **Individual Work** Rewrite your assigned news articles for the broadcast. Present all the facts, answering the questions *who, what, when, where, why,* and *how.* Remember that you will have to shorten each article so that the information can be presented in one or two minutes. Collect visual aids to support your story.

4. **Group Work** Share your broadcast materials with the group. Give one another suggestions for improvements. Together, organize your broadcast and prepare your visual aids. For example, you might want to present statistics on a poster. The weather reporter might use a classroom map to describe the weather in the region. Rehearse your broadcast presentation.

5. **Group Sharing** Present your news broadcast to the class.

6. **Extended Group Work** If you have access to video equipment, make a video of your news broadcasts. Allow each group member to select a day to take the video home to show parents and friends.

Group Process Questions

• What is the most important thing you learned about Japan and the Koreas from this activity?

• How is news reporting different on television from in a newspaper?

• What problems did you have in doing your part of the project?

• How did you solve the problems?

• How was it helpful to work with others?

Quick Check

1. Was the goal of the assignment clear at all times?

_____

2. Did you have problems working well together? If so, how did you solve them?

_____

3. Were you satisfied with your work on the news broadcast? Why or why not?

_____

_____

Chapter Map Activity 7

Teaching Strategy

Japan is an island country off the coast of eastern Asia. Although the country is only about the size of California, it is an economic powerhouse. The Korean Peninsula has long been a bridge between Japan and the rest of Asia. Although Korea is currently divided politically, it has an extensive history as a united country.

Regional and Political Maps

Place Location Activity

Reproduce the regional map for each student. Ask students to:

- Label the following countries and their boundaries: Japan, North Korea, South Korea. Also label the following Japanese islands: Hokkaido, Honshu, Shikoku, Kyushu, Ryukyu Islands, Okinawa.
- Trace the following rivers: Yalu, Tumen, Taedong, Han, Naktong, Teshio, Shinano, Tone.
- Label the following bodies of water: Sea of Japan, Inland Sea, Yellow Sea, East China Sea, Korea Strait, Pacific Ocean.
- With an arrow, indicate on your map in what direction the United States is from this region.

Reproduce the political map for each student. Ask students to:

- Label the countries and bodies of water. *(See the list of countries and bodies of water for the regional map.)*
- Mark and label the national capital and major cities of each country. *(Remind students to include a map key.)*

Discussing the Maps

1. Which is the largest Japanese island? *(Honshu)*
2. Name the two rivers that make up much of North Korea's northern border. *(the Yalu and Tumen Rivers)*
3. In which direction would you travel if you journeyed in a straight line from Sapporo to Kyoto? What is the approximate straight-line distance between the two cities? *(You would travel southwest to journey from Sapporo to Kyoto. The two cities are about 645 miles [1,032 km] apart.)*
4. True or false: The capital of South Korea is Pyongyang. *(False; the capital of South Korea is Seoul. Pyongyang is North Korea's capital.)*
5. Which of the following Japanese islands lies farthest north: Kyushu, Okinawa, Hokkaido, or Shikoku? Which lies farthest south? *(Hokkaido lies farthest north; Okinawa lies farthest south.)*

Physical and Capitals and Major Cities Maps

Place Location Activity

Reproduce the physical map for each student. Ask students to:

- Label the countries, rivers, and bodies of water. *(See the list for the regional map.)*
- Mark and label the major cities of each country.
- Label the following: Korean Peninsula, Taebaek Mountains, Kanto Plain, Cheju Island.

Reproduce the capitals and major cities map for each student. Ask students to:

- Label the countries.
- Label the capital and major cities of each country.

Discussing the Maps

1. Into which body of water does the Han River empty? Where does the river begin? *(The Han River empties into the Yellow Sea. It begins in the Taebaek Mountains.)*
2. True or false: The Inland Sea separates South Korea and Japan. *(False; the Korea Strait separates the countries.)*
3. Where is the Kanto Plain located? Name two major cities found there. *(The Kanto Plain is located on the eastern side of the Japanese island of Honshu. Tokyo and Yokohama are located there.)*
4. Which capital city is located along the Taedong River? *(Pyongyang, North Korea)*
5. Why do you think the population density of Hokkaido is not as heavy as it is in most of the rest of Japan? *(Hokkaido is in northern Japan, where the winters are snowy and much colder than in the rest of the country.)*

APPLYING GEOGRAPHY SKILLS

Japanese Expansion—1914 to 1941

You may use the following activity as a cooperative learning activity or extra credit project.

Divide the class into two groups. Ask one group to create a map showing the expansion of Japan into Asia from 1914 to 1941. Ask the other group to create a time line on the same subject. After the groups have completed their projects, compare the map with the time line and discuss any differences found.

Chapter Map Activity 7

CHAPTER 7

Japan and the Koreas: Regional

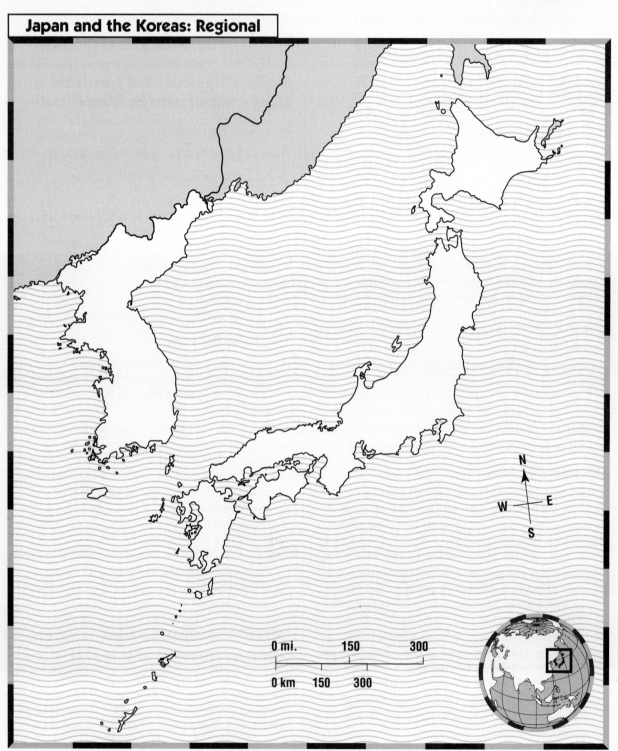

Chapter Map Activity 7

Japan and the Koreas: Political

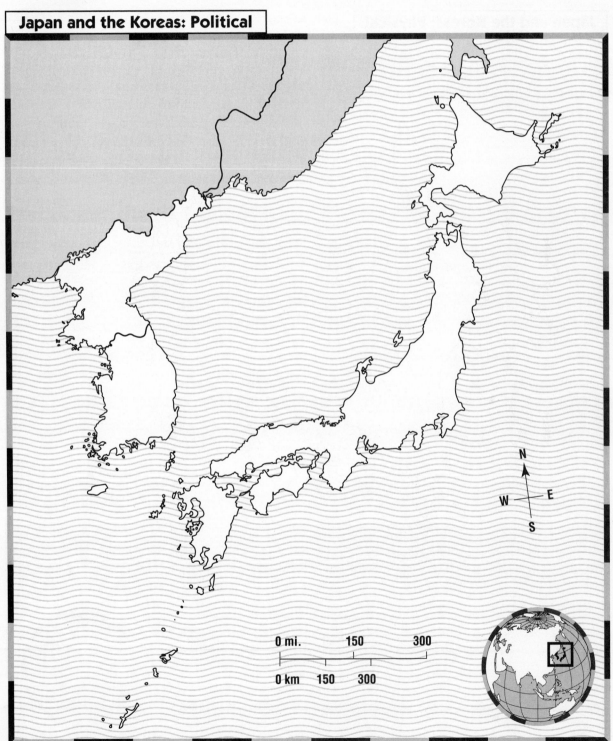

0 mi.   150   300

0 km   150   300

CHAPTER 7

Chapter Map Activity 7

CHAPTER 7

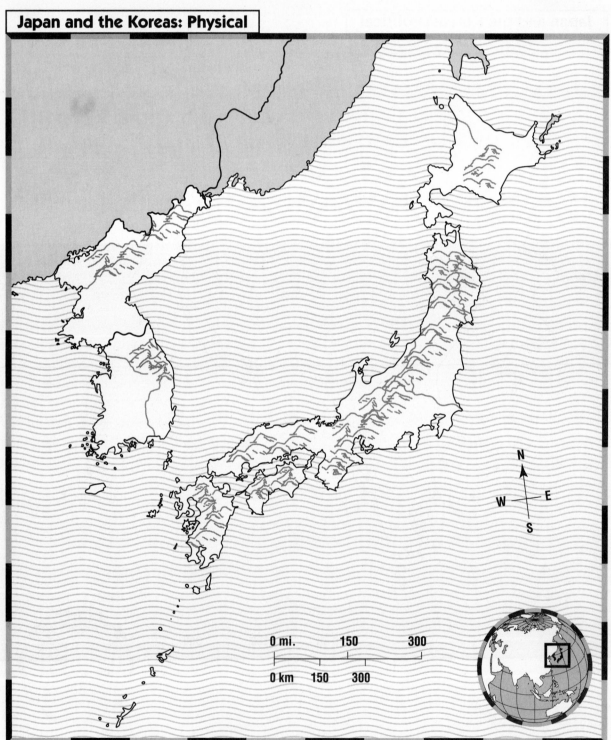

Japan and the Koreas: Physical

Chapter Map Activity 7

Japan and the Koreas: Capitals and Major Cities

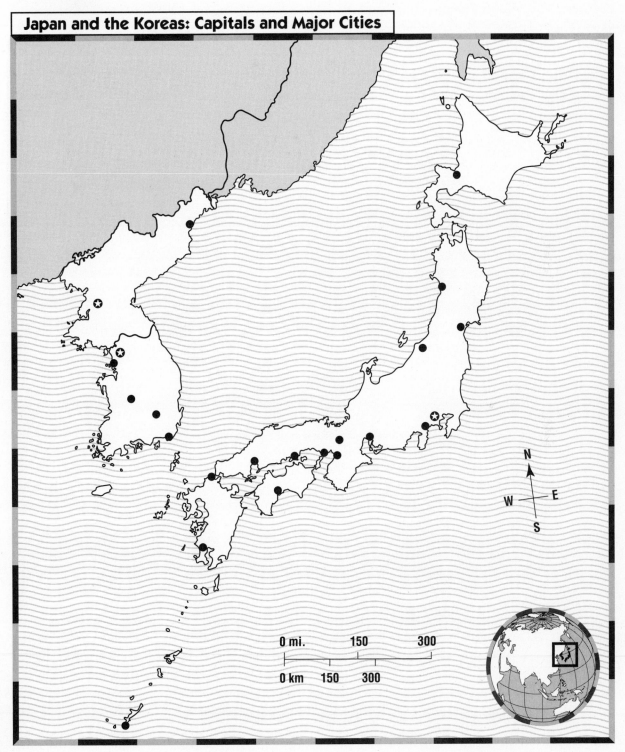

0 mi.   150   300

0 km   150   300

N
W   E
S

CHAPTER 7

Chapter Skills Activity 7

Making Comparisons

Learning the Skill

When you make comparisons, you determine similarities and differences among ideas, objects, or events. To make a comparison, identify or decide what will be compared. Then, decide a common area or areas in which comparisons can be drawn. Finally, look for similarities and differences within these areas.

Practicing the Skill

Directions: Use the graphs below to make comparisons, then answer the following questions.

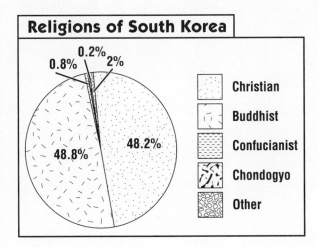

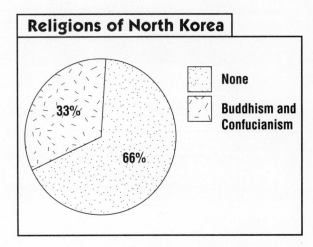

1. What can the two circle graphs be used to compare? _____

2. What are the two main religions of South Korea? _____

3. In which of the two Koreas do people seem to have more religious choices? _____

Applying the Skill

Directions: Survey 10 classmates about their favorite type of music and the type of music their parents prefer. For example, they might prefer country, rap, classical, jazz, or rock. Create two circle graphs on a separate sheet of paper and use your survey results to answer the following questions.

1. What is the most popular type of music of the classmates you surveyed?

2. Why do you think some parents prefer different types of music?

CHAPTER 7

Reteaching Activity 7

Four main islands and thousands of smaller islands make up the country of Japan. Japan is one of the world's major economic and industrial powers. Two countries—North Korea and South Korea—occupy a finger of land between the Sea of Japan and the Yellow Sea. South Korea has surpassed North Korea industrially because of its dynamic free enterprise economy.

DIRECTIONS: Making a Chart Read each word or phrase below. Each item applies to Japan or to one or both of the Koreas. Write each letter in the appropriate box.

JAPAN

THE KOREAS

NORTH | **SOUTH**

A. archipelago	**G.** the Inland Sea	**M.** Silla rulers
B. 38th parallel	**H.** Seoul	**N.** monsoons
C. famine	**I.** tsunamis	**O.** Mt. Fuji
D. peninsula	**J.** Tokyo	**P.** shoguns
E. Yalu River	**K.** intensive cultivation	**Q.** Shinto
F. must import coal	**L.** government-run farms	**R.** Pyongyang

Critical Thinking Skills Activity 7

Determining Cause and Effect

SOCIAL STUDIES OBJECTIVE: Analyze information by identifying cause-and-effect relationships.

Learning the Skill

Determining **cause and effect** means you look for something that makes something else happen—a *cause*. Then you look for the result of the cause or what happened—the *effect*. For example, someone flips a switch in your living room and the overhead light comes on. The person flipping the switch is a cause. The light coming on is an effect. Unusual rain patterns cause the water behind a dam to rise to dangerous levels. The rain is the cause. The dangerous state of the dam is the effect. To better understand any event, you can view it as an "effect" and then examine what you believe to be the cause. In the same way, you can identify the causes of an event and predict what the effects might be. By identifying cause-

and-effect relationships you can get a better understanding of events or situations. To identify cause-and-effect relationships, use these steps:

- Identify an event or situation.
- Compare the situation with conditions before it happened (causes) and after it happened (effects).
- Look for words or terms that help you decide whether one event caused another. Words or phrases such as *brought about, produced, resulted in, when,* and *therefore* indicate cause-and-effect relationships.
- Look for logical relationships between events. Identify the outcomes of events. Remember that some effects have more than one cause, and some causes lead to more than one effect.

Applying the Skill

Directions: When studying the history of a country, filling in a chart can help you understand the causes and effects of events in that country's history. Read the article about Korea below. Then complete the chart by filling in the missing causes or effects. The first cause-and-effect relationship has been given.

KOREA

Although Korea is now divided, it has a long history as a united country. North Korea and South Korea sit on a peninsula between the Sea of Japan and the Yellow Sea. For centuries, the Korean Peninsula was a bridge between Japan and the mainland of Asia. Trade and ideas traveled back and forth. After World War II, troops from the Soviet Union took over northern Korea, and American troops occupied the south. Eventually Korea was divided along the 38th parallel. A Communist government took power in the north while a non-Communist government governed the south. South Korea has more than twice the population of North Korea. South Korea's economy is strong. North Korea, however, struggles with poverty and food shortages. Most South Koreans practice Christianity, Buddhism, or the teachings of Confucius. Religion is discouraged in North Korea.

Critical Thinking Skills Activity 7 (continued)

Cause	→	Effect
Korean Peninsula was a bridge between Japan and mainland Asia.	→	Trade and ideas traveled back and forth between Korea and mainland Asia.
	→	Korea divided along 38th parallel.
Communist government took power in North Korea.	→	
Non-Communist government took power in South Korea.	→	

Practicing the Skill

Directions: Read the paragraphs below. Then answer the questions that follow by circling the letter of the correct answer.

> After World War II, Japan stopped all military activity for more than 50 years. Japan is now beginning to take a more active security role in East Asia. Instead of relying on the United States to take care of problems, Japan is taking its own action. During the 1990s, several events occurred that caused Japan to take security issues more seriously. These events included:
>
> * China's attempt to bully Taiwan in 1996.
> * North Korea's missile launch in 1998.
> * President Bill Clinton's consideration of forming a "strategic partnership" between the United States and China in 1998.
>
> As a result, Japan has started gathering and evaluating intelligence (military information) on its own. This effort includes setting up a network of spies. Japan has also taken more interest in developments in North and South Korea.

1. What event did NOT cause Japan to take a more aggressive security role in East Asia?

A. North Korea's missile launch in 1998.

B. The start of a new millennium in the year 2000.

C. China's attempt to bully Taiwan in 1996.

D. President Clinton's "strategic partnership" plan with China in 1998.

2. What is NOT an effect of Japan's more aggressive security role?

A. Japan set up a network of spies.

B. Japan is gathering and evaluating intelligence information.

C. Japan is paying more attention to North and South Korea.

D. Japan is economically successful.

Map and Graph Skills Activity 7
Comparing a Map and a Graph

NATIONAL GEOGRAPHY STANDARD 9: The geographically informed person knows and understands the characteristics, distribution, and migration of human populations on Earth's surface.

 ## Learning the Skill

A map and a graph both show you a picture, but in different ways. Maps show locations, while graphs display information—usually data in numbers—about those locations. Comparing maps and graphs can help you understand more about a region. It can also show relationships between those regions. To compare a map and a graph, follow these steps:

- Read the map and graph titles to see how the two are related.
- On the map, locate places included in the graph.
- Use information on the graph to draw conclusions about the places on the map. Use the map to help explain the information on the graph.

Applying the Skill

Directions: The map shows the major Asian Pacific Rim countries. The circle graph illustrates the population distribution among these countries. (Note: The total population of these countries is approximately 1.48 billion.) If you compare such a graph with a map, you can learn about population density. Study the map and graph and use them to answer the questions on the next page in the spaces provided.

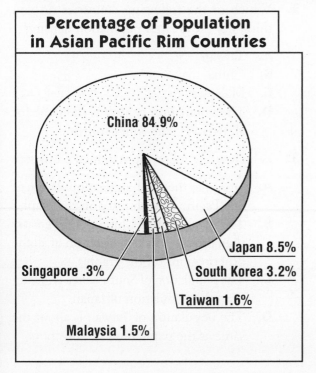

Percentage of Population in Asian Pacific Rim Countries

China 84.9%
Japan 8.5%
South Korea 3.2%
Taiwan 1.6%
Singapore .3%
Malaysia 1.5%

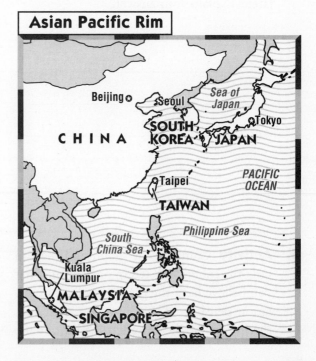

Asian Pacific Rim

Beijing
Seoul
Sea of Japan
CHINA
SOUTH KOREA
JAPAN
Tokyo
PACIFIC OCEAN
Taipei
TAIWAN
Philippine Sea
South China Sea
Kuala Lumpur
MALAYSIA
SINGAPORE

1. Which country shown has the largest population?

_____

_____

2. Which country has the smallest population?

_____

_____

3. Which country's population is about the same size as Malaysia's?

_____

4. True or False: The population of Malaysia is less than twice the size of Singapore's population.

_____

5. **Critical Thinking** From the map, note that Japan and Malaysia are almost the same size physically. Use the graph to find the population percentages of the two countries. Which country is the most densely populated? Explain your answer.

_____

_____

_____

_____

_____

6. **Activity** Compare the graph and map to rank the countries listed in order from what you believe have the greatest to least population densities. Then, use your textbook, the library, or the Internet to find out the

actual population densities of these countries. Were your guesses correct? Explain.

_____

_____

_____

_____

_____

Practicing the Skill

Directions: Answer the following questions based on the map and graph by circling the letter of the correct answer.

1. The three most populous Asian Pacific Rim countries, in order, are

A. Japan, South Korea, Taiwan.
B. China, South Korea, Taiwan.
C. China, Japan, South Korea.
D. China, Taiwan, Japan.

2. Which of the following countries do you think has the greatest population density?

A. Taiwan
B. China
C. Malaysia
D. The population density is the same for all Asian Pacific Rim countries.

3. Which of the following statements is true?

A. Japan has the third-largest population of any Pacific Rim country on the graph.
B. The population of China alone is greater than the combined population of all the other regions on the graph.
C. The population of South Korea is greater than the population of Japan.
D. The population of Taiwan is about the same as the population of Singapore.

Reading and Writing Skills Activity 7
Locating Articles in Newspapers and Other Periodicals

SOCIAL STUDIES OBJECTIVE: To research and locate current information on a topic in newspapers, magazines, and journals.

Learning the Skill

Newspapers, magazines, and journals are good sources of information on recent events. You can also use these sources to find editorials of past events to understand what people thought of an event at the time. If you want to find the most current information, make sure that you use the most current articles available. Use the following resources to help you find an article in a newspaper or periodical.

1. **Computer databases** You may be able to use the library's computers to locate magazine and newspaper articles on your topic. These articles are organized and stored in a database. The library may store databases on CD-ROMs, or it may subscribe to an online service that provides databases. Some libraries do both. You can search by topic, by type of publication (magazine or newspaper), or by specific publication. You begin by entering a key word, and the database will list articles about that topic. The listing usually includes the title, the author, the publication, the date, and a sentence or two about the article. Select the articles that seem useful. The database will then allow you to read a brief summary or the whole article on the computer screen. For a small fee, you can print a copy of the article.

2. *Readers' Guide to Periodical Literature* Not every library has computer databases, but nearly every library has the print edition of the *Readers' Guide to Periodical Literature.* This guide includes titles of articles from about 200 magazines and journals. Subjects are listed alphabetically and are cross-referenced. An update of the print edition of

Readers' Guide is published every two weeks. Information about all articles published that year is reprinted in a hardbound book at the end of the year. The guide is also available on a CD-ROM that you can search using a computer.

3. **Microfilm and microfiche** Libraries often keep issues for the current year in their newspapers and periodicals section. Issues from the previous one to five years may be stored in a different area. Older issues may be on microfilm, which is a roll or reel of film, or microfiche, which is a sheet of film. Both types of film must be inserted into special projectors that enlarge the pages so that you can read them easily. You can usually make copies of these articles to take home. Use the computer database or the *Readers' Guide* to find information about articles that may be on microfilm or microfiche to narrow your search.

4. **Internet** Many newspapers and magazines have a Web site that has an online version of their print counterpart. Some of these sites allow you to search their database for articles by topic. You may encounter sites in which you have to be a subscriber to the site and pay a subscription fee to be able to access the articles. If you do not know which newspapers or magazines may have articles on your topic, try doing a key word search on your favorite Internet search engine. The search results should list summaries of the sites. These summaries should help you decide which sites may help you with your research. If you have any questions or concerns when searching through library resources, be sure to ask a librarian for help.

JAPAN AND THE KOREAS
Reading and Writing Skills Activity 7 (continued)

Applying the Skill

Directions: Suppose you are writing a report on Japan and/or the Koreas and you need additional information. Think of resources you could use for researching newspaper and magazine articles and answer the following questions in the space provided. Try to use a different resource for each topic.

1. How could you research current politics in Japan?

_____

_____

2. How could you research Japan's military strategies in World War II?

_____

_____

3. How could you research the current state of relations between North Korea and South Korea?

_____

_____

4. How could you research the current state of the South Korean economy?

_____

_____

Practicing the Skill

Directions: Answer the following questions by circling the letter of the correct answer.

1. Which of the following is a way to search for newspaper and magazine articles?
   A. through computer databases
   B. using *Readers' Guide to Periodical Literature*
   C. using microfiche and microfilm
   D. all of the above

2. What is microfilm?
   A. a sheet of film   **C.** a short movie
   B. a roll or reel of film   **D.** a computer database

GeoLab Activity 7

Talking Origami

From the classroom of Dana Moseley, Carl Stuart Middle School, Conway, Arkansas

The Japanese developed origami, the ancient art of paper folding, in the early 700s. Learn more about origami, and then make your own paper-folding project.

Background

The Japanese incorporate art into their daily lives. They emphasize the beauty of water, trees, soil, flowers, and animals. Paper has long been used in Japan in ways different from other cultures. The Japanese traditionally built houses with windows made of paper, and they invented the paper umbrella. The ancient art form of paper folding, origami, has been used by the Japanese to make patterns for incredible objects and animals from a simple piece of paper. The secret of origami is to fold the paper once, and then fold the same piece again, again, and again. The story, *Sadako and the Thousand Paper Cranes*, tells about the horrors of World War II in Japan contrasted with the beauty of the country's art. Read this story, and find out more about the art of origami by creating a paper crane (as shown below).

Materials

- book, *Sadako and the Thousand Paper Cranes*, by Eleanor Coerr
- 4" × 4" square of origami paper, colored on one side (optional)
- diagrams for folding paper crane (below)
- map of Japan
- contemporary Japanese music (optional)

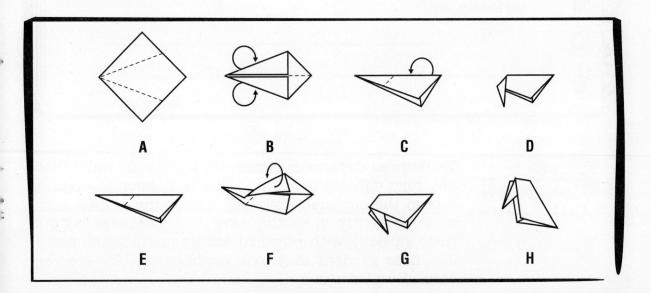

A

B

C

D

E

F

G

H

JAPAN AND THE KOREAS

GeoLab Activity 7 (continued)

What to Do

1. (optional) Read the story about Sadako. Discuss the story with the class.
2. Refer to a map of Japan, and possibly play Japanese music as you prepare to make the origami project.
3. Follow the step-by-step diagram on the previous page for creating an origami paper crane.

Lab Activity Report

1. What feelings or emotions did you feel as you read the Sadako story?

   _____

   _____

2. Were you able to easily follow the folding diagrams? Why or why not?

   _____

   _____

3. Why do you think the Japanese often use paper colored on only one side for origami?

   _____

4. **Drawing Conclusions** How is origami different from art forms that you are familiar with?

   _____

   _____

Traditional Japanese homes are built with walls that are very delicate and light. This is to keep the homes cool in the summer. This also makes the homes crumple lightly in earthquakes. The Japanese lay out their gardens with physical accuracy. Although some Japanese gardens may look haphazard, they are very carefully planned.

Enrichment Activity 7

Earthquakes and Volcanoes in Japan

CHAPTER 7

Directions: Read the following information about Japan. Then answer the questions that follow on a separate sheet of paper.

Huge upward movements of the earth's crust formed the island of Japan. Today giant movements still take place in the earth below Japan. As a result, Japan is a land of earthquakes. Every year about 5,000 earthquakes jolt the people of Japan. Most earthquakes are minor and cause little damage. When strong earthquakes hit the islands, however, they cause terrible damage and kill many people. In 1948, for example, an earthquake destroyed an entire city on the island of Honshu. In 1995, an earthquake struck the city of Kobe, causing widespread damage and killing more than 5,000 people.

The worst earthquake in modern times struck Japan in 1923. The country's largest cities, Tokyo and Yokohama, suffered terrible losses. The fires caused by the earthquake destroyed large parts of Tokyo. More than 130,000 Japanese died.

The Japanese have learned to live with the earthquakes. Today, buildings are constructed to withstand all but the most powerful earthquakes. Children in school have earthquake drills that help them find the safest place to survive an earthquake.

Earthquakes in the ocean near Japan's coast sometimes cause huge sea waves called **tsunamis.** Waves as high as 100 feet (30.5 m) may suddenly slam against Japanese seashore towns. In 1983, a tsunami struck Honshu's coast, killing 100 people.

The giant movements of the earth's crust that formed Japan also create volcanoes. Japan's four main islands have 200 volcanoes. About 30 of these volcanoes still erupt from time to time. Japan's highest, best known mountain is Mount Fuji, a volcano that is no longer active.

How Earthquakes Cause Tsunamis

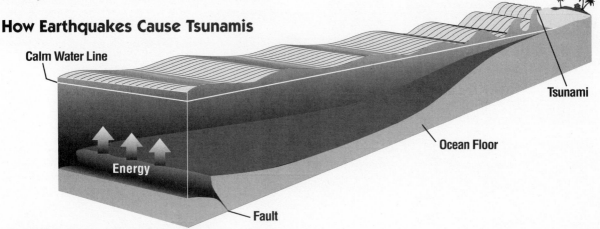

Calm Water Line

Tsunami

Energy

Ocean Floor

Fault

Taking Another Look

1. What causes a tsunami to form?
2. From the diagram, what happens when a fault opens on the ocean floor?
3. Imagine that you are a young person who lives in Kobe. Write a diary entry telling about what you and your family did when the earthquake struck at 5:46 A.M. on January 16, 1995.
4. **Expressing Problems Clearly** What natural dangers do the people of Japan face?

OUR WORLD TODAY
People, Places, and Issues

Chapter 7, Section Resources

SECTIONS

JAPAN AND THE KOREAS

Guided Reading Activity 7-1

Japan

DIRECTIONS: Answering Questions Reading the section and answering the questions below will help you learn more about the country of Japan. Use your textbook to write answers to the questions.

1. Why does Japan experience so many earthquakes and tsunamis?

_____

2. What makes up Japan's land area?

_____

3. What is Japan known for in industry?

_____

4. What do Japanese farmers practice?

_____

5. What are Japan's economic challenges?

_____

_____

6. Where do the Japanese trace their ancestry?

_____

7. Who ruled Japan after the emperors' power declined?

_____

8. Where do most of the people live?

_____

9. What do the two major religions of Japan teach?

_____

_____

10. What Japanese sports have origins in the past?

_____

Name _____ Date _____ Class _____

Guided Reading Activity 7-2

The Two Koreas

DIRECTIONS: Reading for Accuracy Reading the section and completing the activity below will help you learn more about North Korea and South Korea. Use your textbook to decide if a statement is true or false. Write **T** or **F,** and if a statement is false, rewrite it correctly.

_____ **1.** Korea was originally ruled by China.

_____

_____ **2.** Korea has always been independent.

_____

_____ **3.** Korea has been separated since the end of World War II.

_____

_____

_____ **4.** After the Korean War, Korea reunited.

_____

_____ **5.** Monsoons affect the climate of South Korea.

_____

_____

_____ **6.** South Korea's economy is dominated by agriculture.

_____

_____ **7.** Farming in North Korea provides food for the whole country.

_____

_____ **8.** People of both Koreas belong to the same ethnic group.

_____

_____ **9.** Mountains run through the majority of North Korea.

_____

_____ **10.** The North Korean government discourages the practice of religion.

_____

Chapter 8 Resources

SOUTHEAST ASIA

Vocabulary Activity 8

DIRECTIONS: Fill in the Blanks Select a term from below to fill in each blank in the following sentences.

plate   deforestation   free port
monsoons   civil war   strait
socialism   delta   terraced fields
precious gems

1. Indonesia sprawls over an area where two huge slabs of rock that make up the earth's crust meet. A slab of rock is known as a tectonic _____.

2. The city of Singapore has a _____, where goods can be loaded or unloaded, stored, and shipped again without payment of import taxes.

3. Myanmar's economic system, known as _____, means that most businesses are owned and run by the government.

4. Myanmar exports _____ like rubies, sapphires, and jade that are sold for high prices.

5. In the Philippines, farmers have cut strips of land out of the hillside like stair steps to make _____.

6. Myanmar's tropical and subtropical climates are influenced by seasonal winds called _____.

7. West of Malaya lies a narrow body of water called the _____ of Malacca.

8. In north Vietnam, soil deposits have formed a fertile _____ at the mouth of the Red River.

9. Since the 1960s, _____, or fighting among different groups within a country, has occurred on several of the islands of Indonesia.

10. Due to the widespread cutting of its trees, or _____, Myanmar's forests are decreasing.

CHAPTER 8

Cooperative Learning Activity 8

Ring of Fire

Background

A volcano is an opening in the earth's crust, either on land or under the oceans. Volcanoes sometimes explode, throwing lava (melted rock), hot rocks, and gases into the air. Most volcanoes are found along a belt, called the Ring of Fire, that surrounds the Pacific Ocean. The islands of Southeast Asia lie along this belt. The people on these islands live under a constant threat of volcanic activity, yet the volcanoes also provide rich soil for farming.

Group Directions

1. Use Chapter 8 and library resources or the Internet to find out as much as you can about the Southeast Asian islands on the Ring of Fire.

2. Write a descriptive report about one of the islands affected by volcanoes, and create a map showing the locations of the volcanoes and cities.

3. Consider the following aspects of living near a volcano, as well as any other facts you find during your research:

> how the island was formed
> active and dormant volcanoes on the island
> settlements near volcanoes
> benefits of living near a volcano
> recent volcanic activity
> results of eruptions

Organizing the Group

1. **Decision Making** As a group, decide which Southeast Asian island country to research. Use the suggestions in the box above to decide what to include in your project. Also decide how to divide up the work among group members.

2. **Individual Work** Do research on your assigned parts of the project and take notes on what you discover.

3. **Group Work/Decision Making** Share your research with the group. As a group, choose which parts to include in the group's final report.

SOUTHEAST ASIA

Cooperative Learning Activity 8 (continued)

4. **Additional Group Work** Together, create a map of the country, showing volcanoes and settlements. Write your final report.

5. **Group Sharing** Display your map in the classroom along with those of other groups. Locate your country on a regional map of the Ring of Fire that's also displayed. Hand in your reports to your teacher, or give them orally, as instructed by your teacher. If you give oral reports, make sure that all group members take part.

Group Process Questions

• What is the most important thing you learned about volcanoes' effects on Southeast Asia from this activity?

• What part of the project did you enjoy most?

• What problems did you have?

• How did you solve the problems?

• How was it helpful to work with others?

Quick Check

1. Was the goal of the assignment clear at all times?

_____

_____

2. Did you have problems working well together? If so, how did you solve them?

_____

_____

3. Were you happy with your part of the map and report? Why or why not?

_____

_____

_____

Chapter Map Activity 8
Teaching Strategy

The peninsulas and islands that make up Southeast Asia cover an area of about 1.7 million square miles (4.5 million sq. km). The region is made up of a wide variety of cultures, types of governments, and economic activities. Much of the world's rice is grown in the fertile soil of mainland Southeast Asia, and the city of Singapore is a thriving commercial center.

Regional and Political Maps

Place Location Activity

Reproduce the regional map for each student. Ask students to:
- Label the following countries and their boundaries: Myanmar, Thailand, Laos, Vietnam, Cambodia, Malaysia, Singapore, Brunei, Indonesia, Philippines, and East Timor.
- Trace the following rivers: Chindwin, Irrawaddy, Salween, Mekong.
- Label the following bodies of water: South China Sea, Philippine Sea, Java Sea, Celebes Sea, Gulf of Tonkin, Indian Ocean, Pacific Ocean.
- With an arrow, indicate on your map in what direction the United States is from this region.

Reproduce the political map for each student. Ask students to:
- Label the countries and bodies of water. *(See the list of countries and bodies of water for the regional map.)*
- Mark and label the national capital and major cities of each country. *(Remind students to include a map key.)*

Discussing the Maps

1. Which countries constitute mainland Southeast Asia? *(Myanmar, Thailand, Laos, Cambodia, and Vietnam)*
2. Name the river that makes up much of the border between Laos and Thailand. *(the Mekong River)*
3. What is the approximate straight-line distance between Bangkok and Ho Chi Minh City? *(The two cities are about 475 miles [760 km] apart.)*
4. The Irrawaddy and Salween Rivers flow through which Southeast Asian country? *(Myanmar)*
5. List the following capital cities in order from northernmost to southernmost: Yangon, Kuala Lumpur, Dili, Phnom Penh, Hanoi. *(Hanoi, Yangon, Phnom Penh, Kuala Lumpur, Dili)*
6. Malaysia consists of what two landforms? *(peninsula and island)*

Physical and Capitals and Major Cities Maps

Place Location Activity

Reproduce the physical map for each student. Ask students to:
- Label the countries, rivers, and bodies of water. *(See the list for the regional map.)*
- Mark and label the major cities of each country.
- Label the following: Luzon, Mindoro, Mindanao, Isthmus of Kra, Malay Peninsula, Barisan Mountains, Sumatra, Java, Bali, Borneo, Celebes, Moluccas, New Guinea.

Reproduce the capitals and major cities map for each student. Ask students to:
- Label the countries.
- Label the capital and major cities of each country.

Discussing the Maps

1. Into which body of water does the Mekong River flow? *(The Mekong River flows into the South China Sea.)*
2. All or part of three different countries are located on the island of Borneo. Name them. *(Malaysia, Brunei, and Indonesia)*
3. Which of the following does not belong in the list: Sumatra, Java, Mindanao, Bali? Explain your answer. *(All but Mindanao are part of Indonesia; Mindanao is part of the Philippines.)*
4. Are any Southeast Asian countries landlocked? If so, name them. *(Laos is the only landlocked Southeast Asian country.)*

APPLYING GEOGRAPHY SKILLS
Mapping Religious Centers

You may use the following activity as a cooperative learning activity or extra credit project.

Divide the class into groups and ask each to find the location of the following religious centers or shrines: Pagan, Pegu, Dagon, Angkor, Ayutthaya, Indrapura, Pasai, Malacca, Borobudur, Bali. Each group should indicate the location of each center on a Southeast Asian map, using special symbols to denote the appropriate religion.

CHAPTER 8

Chapter Map Activity 8

CHAPTER 8

Southeast Asia: Regional

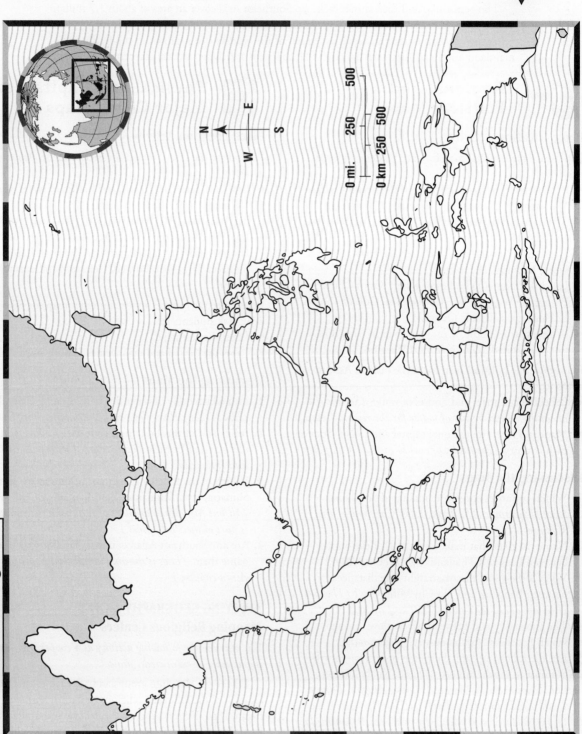

Chapter Map Activity 8

Southeast Asia: Political

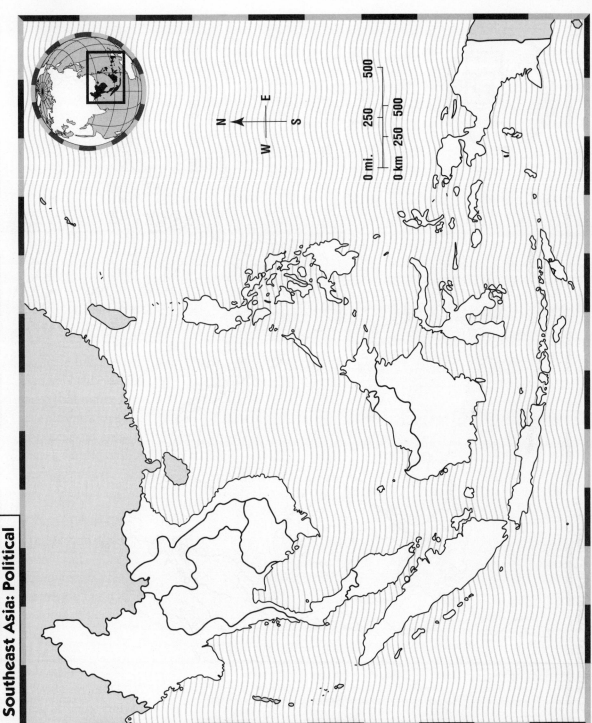

CHAPTER 8

Chapter Map Activity 8

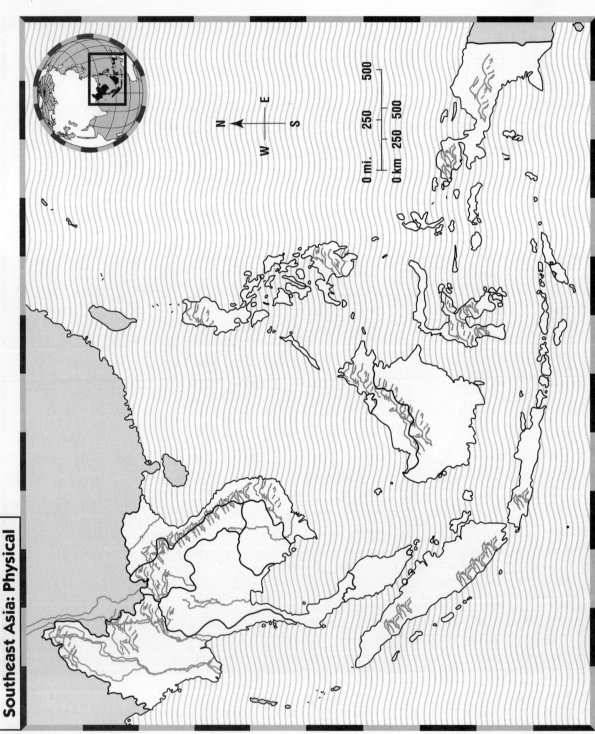

Southeast Asia: Physical

Chapter Map Activity 8

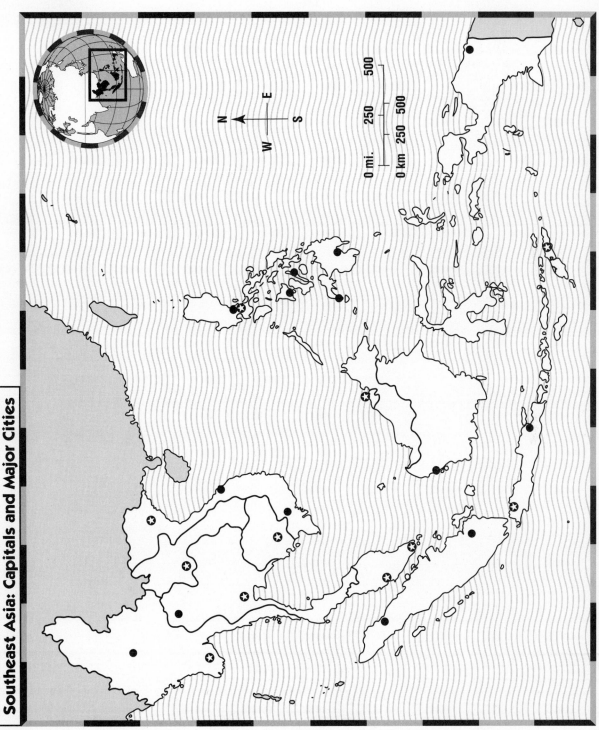

Southeast Asia: Capitals and Major Cities

CHAPTER 8

Chapter Map Activity 8

Chapter Skills Activity 8

Reading a Contour Map

 ## Learning the Skill

Contour maps use lines, called isolines, to outline the shape—or contour—of the landscape. To read a contour map, first identify the area shown on the map. Read the numbers on the isolines to determine how much the elevation increases or decreases with each line. Notice the amount of space between the lines, which tells you whether the land is steep or flat. (When the lines are far apart, the land rises gradually. Where the lines are close together, the land rises steeply.)

Practicing the Skill

Directions: Study the contour map below, then answer the following questions on a separate sheet of paper.

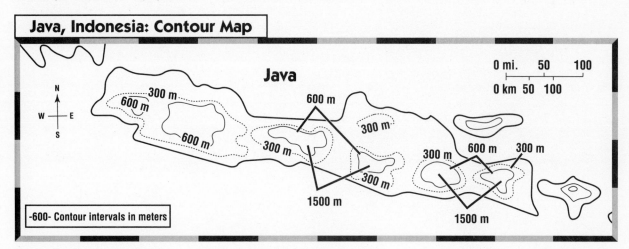

Java, Indonesia: Contour Map

1. What area of Southeast Asia is shown on the map?
2. What elevations are shown on the map?
3. What kind of slope would you expect to see if the isolines are far apart? If they are close together?

Applying the Skill

Directions: Using your local library resources or the Internet, find a contour map for your state. Use this map to answer the following questions on a separate sheet of paper.

1. What elevations are shown on the isolines of the map?
2. What is the lowest elevation on the map? The highest?
3. Is the terrain represented on the map generally steep or flat?

117

Name _____ Date _____ Class _____

Reteaching Activity 8

Peninsulas and archipelagos form Southeast Asia. All but one of the countries is a former European colony. Although the mainland penin- sula countries share similar landforms, and the archipelago nations share tropical climates, each has a distinct culture.

DIRECTIONS: Filling in the Blanks On the line before each statement, write the name of the country the statement best describes.

- Indonesia
- Laos
- Brunei
- Thailand
- Philippines
- Singapore
- Cambodia
- Myanmar
- Vietnam
- Malaysia

1. _____ This "land of the free" was never a European colony. Its gov- ernment is taking steps to limit deforestation.

2. _____ Income from oil and natural gas provide a high living stan- dard for this nation. The people enjoy free education and health care.

3. _____ This island nation is a world leader in rubber and palm oil production. It has a large Chinese population.

4. _____ One of the world's smallest countries boasts one of the world's most productive economies. Its capital is a busy free port.

5. _____ This landlocked Communist country is covered by mountains and has electricity in only a few cities.

6. _____ This nation is an archipelago of more than 7,000 islands. It has a culture that blends Malay, Spanish, and American influences.

7. _____ Fighting between a Communist government in the north and an American-supported government in the south led to war in this country in the 1960s.

8. _____ The largest Southeast Asian country has the fourth-largest population in the world. It is an archipelago of more than 13,600 islands.

9. _____ About 75 percent of the world's teakwood comes from this Buddhist nation, formerly known as Burma.

10. _____ A harsh communist government took control of this once pro- ductive nation in the mid-1970s. Under its rule, more than 1 million people died. Most of its nearly 12 million people belong to the Khmer ethnic group.

Critical Thinking Skills Activity 8

Comparing Points of View

SOCIAL STUDIES OBJECTIVE: Identify participants' points of view from the historical and/or cultural context surrounding an event.

 ## Learning the Skill

A **point of view** is an opinion or belief about something. A person's point of view often affects the way he or she interprets a topic or event. It is important to recognize, or interpret, an author's point of view when you are using information. Much of history is the story of people with different viewpoints and how the differences between them were resolved. To understand history, as well as current issues, you must compare points of view on issues. To compare points of view, use the following steps:

- Read the material to identify the general subject.
- Identify the different viewpoints. Determine what aspect of the issue each viewpoint stresses.
- Ask the same questions about each point of view as you study it.
- Analyze how the answers to these questions are similar or different.

Applying the Skill

Directions: Read these statements by two people who were involved in different ways with the Vietnam War. Then answer the following questions on the lines below.

"The principal lesson of the Vietnam War is that the United States should not intervene [interfere] in other countries with military forces unless that country is a serious threat to our own [country's] security. We should not use military force to dictate [determine] the political system of another country—especially small countries that wish to have a political system different from ours."

—J. William Fulbright,
U.S. senator from
Arkansas, 1945–1974

"First, the Vietnam War was not a civil war, nor a South Vietnamese insurgency [uprising]. Second, our motives for helping the South Vietnamese were moral. We wanted to prevent a small democracy from being subjugated [controlled] by a communist state by force of arms. The United States wanted no territory in Vietnam, none of its scarce resources, and no military bases there."

—Phillip Davidson, Jr.,
veteran of World War II,
Korean War, Vietnam War

1. According to Senator Fulbright, why was the United States not justified in entering the Vietnam War?

_____

_____

_____

_____

2. According to Phillip Davidson, why was the United States justified in entering the Vietnam War?

_____

_____

_____

_____

CHAPTER 8

SOUTHEAST ASIA

Critical Thinking Skills Activity 8 (continued)

3. What is the major difference between Senator Fulbright's point of view and Phillip Davidson's point of view?

_____

_____

_____

_____

4. With which of the two points of view do you agree? Does the author's background influence your decision? If so, how?

_____

_____

_____

_____

Practicing the Skill

Directions: Read the following quote by Barry Goldwater about the Vietnam War. Then answer the questions that follow by circling the letter of each correct answer.

> "If we could have stopped communism in Asia, it would have been a gigantic step forward… When President Eisenhower first sent advisors to South Vietnam, with no idea of going to war, I thought it was a good thing. When President Kennedy sent 15,000 Marines and told them to shoot back, I was bothered, because there was no real decision made at the presidential level to win the war. When you decide to go to war, you must at the same instant decide to win it. It's just like having a fight with another fellow: if you go into it halfheartedly, you're going to get the daylights beat out of you. That's what happened in Vietnam."

> —Barry Goldwater,
> U.S. senator from Arizona
> 1953–1965, 1969–1987

1. Senator Goldwater objected to the United States's involvement in the Vietnam War because

   A. he believed that war is evil.
   B. there was no decision to win the war.
   C. he was afraid of losing the war.
   D. he believed Vietnam was too small to pick on.

2. What kind of involvement in Vietnam seemed reasonable to Goldwater?

   A. sending advisors to Vietnam
   B. sending the Marines to Vietnam
   C. declaring war on Vietnam
   D. beating the daylights out of the Vietnamese

3. Senator Goldwater might have agreed that the United States

   A. should not have sent advisors to Vietnam.
   B. should not have declared war.
   C. was justified in entering the Vietnam War.
   D. was not justified in entering the Vietnam War.

4. According to Senator Goldwater, the United States did not win the Vietnam War because

   A. we did not use nuclear weapons.
   B. the Vietnamese fought dirty.
   C. Vietnam's jungles were too thick.
   D. we fought halfheartedly.

Name _____ Date _____ Class _____

Map and Graph Skills Activity 8

Using Technology: Using the Internet

NATIONAL GEOGRAPHY STANDARDS 1 AND 10: The geographically informed person knows how to use technology to answer and pose questions and understands the characteristics, distribution, and complexity of Earth's cultural mosaics.

 ## Learning the Skill

You can learn about almost any topic you can think of by using the Internet, which is a global network of computers. Commercial "search engines" such as AltaVista or Google can help you find information if you do not know exactly where to look for it. To use the Internet to find out about the religions of Southeast Asia, follow these steps:

• Log on to the Internet and access a search engine of your choice.

• Search by typing "Southeast Asia religions" into the search engine.

• Scroll the list of Web pages that appears when the search is complete. Select a page to read or print.

• Continue selecting sites until you have found enough information to complete the activity below. (Hint: If you cannot find any appropriate sites, try the CIA World Factbook site at http://www.odci.gov/cia/publications/factbook/index.html)

Applying the Skill

Directions: Search the Internet to find out the major religions for each of the Southeast Asian countries shown on the map. Assign each religion a color or shading of your choice and fill in the map key accordingly. Then color or shade each country on the map with the appropriate religion. Finally, use your completed map to answer the questions on the next page in the spaces provided.

Southeast Asia: Major Religions

□ BUDDHISM
□ ISLAM
□ CHRISTIANITY

ASIA

MYANMAR · LAOS · Hanoi · Vientiane · Yangon · THAILAND · Bangkok · CAMBODIA · VIETNAM · Phnom Penh · Manila · PHILIPPINES · MALAYSIA · Kuala Lumpur · BRUNEI · Bandar Seri Begawan · SINGAPORE · INDONESIA · Jakarta

SOUTHEAST ASIA

Map and Graph Skills Activity 8 (continued)

1. What is the major religion in most Southeast Asian countries?

   _____

2. How many Southeast Asian countries are primarily Muslim? Name them.

   _____

   _____

   _____

3. What is unusual about the main religion of the Philippines, compared to other Southeast Asian countries?

   _____

   _____

   _____

4. Which religion is a resident of Hanoi most likely to practice?

   _____

5. True or False: The major religion of Cambodia is the same as the major religion of Malaysia.

   _____

6. **Critical Thinking** From your completed map, what general conclusion can you draw about the religious practices of mainland Southeast Asia as opposed to the religious practices on the islands of Southeast Asia?

   _____

   _____

   _____

   _____

7. **Activity** Use the Internet to determine the other religions (besides the major religion) practiced in each Southeast Asian country shown on the map. On a separate sheet of paper, make a list of each country and the other religions that are practiced there.

Practicing the Skill

Directions: Use your completed map to answer the following questions by circling the letter of the correct answer.

1. Christianity is most likely to be practiced by a resident of

   A. Bangkok.
   B. Jakarta.
   C. Singapore.
   D. Manila.

2. Which of the following religions is not a predominant religion in any Southeast Asian country?

   A. Buddhism
   B. Hinduism
   C. Islam
   D. Christianity

3. Which of the following is a predominantly Muslim country?

   A. Vietnam
   B. Laos
   C. Indonesia
   D. Philippines

4. Which religion is most likely practiced by a resident of Yangon?

   A. Buddhism
   B. Christianity
   C. Islam
   D. traditional religion

Reading and Writing Skills Activity 8
Using Other Reference Sources

SOCIAL STUDIES OBJECTIVE: To research and locate other reference sources to research report topics.

Learning the Skill

General reference sources are easy to use and provide information on thousands of topics. The following chart illustrates some examples of reference sources. Some of these are available in CD-ROM format or on the Internet, as well as in print versions.

Type of Reference	Examples
General Encyclopedias–General encyclopedias fill many volumes. Subjects are arranged alphabetically. An index at the end helps you find topics.	*World Book Encyclopedia* *Encyclopedia Britannica* *Encarta Encyclopedia*
Specialized Encyclopedias–Specialized encyclopedias focus on specific topics. You might be surprised at the number of specialized encyclopedias available.	*Encyclopedia of World Art* *Encyclopedia of the Geological Sciences* *Van Nostrand's Scientific Encyclopedia*
Almanacs and Yearbooks–Almanacs and yearbooks are usually published annually. They provide current facts and statistics. Check the most recent issues for the latest information.	*Information Please Almanac* *World Almanac and Book of Facts* *Guinness Book of Records* *Statistical Abstract of the United States*
Atlases–Atlases may contain current or historical information. They include maps and statistics about countries, climates, and other topics.	*Hammond World Atlas* *Cambridge Atlas of Astronomy* *Historical Atlas of the United States* *Atlas of World Cultures*
Biographical References–Biographical reference works include brief histories of notable people, living or dead.	*Contemporary Authors* *Webster's New Biographical Dictionary* *Biographical Dictionary of Scientists (by field)*
Government Publications–Some large libraries have government publications on agriculture, population, economics, and other topics.	*Monthly Catalog of United States Government Publications* *United States Government Publications Catalog*
Books of Quotations–In a book of quotations, you can find quotations by famous people or about certain subjects.	*Bartlett's Familiar Quotations* *The International Thesaurus of Quotations* *The Harper Book of Quotations*

CHAPTER 8

SOUTHEAST ASIA

Reading and Writing Skills Activity 8 (continued)

Applying the Skill

Directions: Read the following topics and list all possible reference resources you may use to research the topic.

1. Socialism in Myanmar

_____

_____

2. Ferdinand Magellan

_____

_____

3. bauxite

_____

_____

4. Ho Chi Minh City

_____

_____

5. the Vietnam War

_____

_____

Practicing the Skill

Directions: Circle the letter of the correct answer.

1. In which of the following references would you find information about Buddhism?
   A. *World Book Encyclopedia*
   B. *Historical Atlas of the United States*
   C. *Contemporary Authors*
   D. all of the above

2. Which of the following resources includes maps and statistics about countries, climates, and other topics?
   A. general encyclopedias
   B. government publications
   C. atlases
   D. books of quotations

GeoLab Activity 8

Celebrate Cultural Differences

From the classroom of Avi Black, San Francisco Unified School District, San Francisco, California

People the world over share many similarities, but there are also many differences. Learn about some of these varying personality and cultural traits as you discover the special intrigue of Southeast Asia.

Background

The countries and people of Southeast Asia have a rich culture and history. They share many similarities, yet each is unique. As a class, you will explore the cultural universals of these countries. A **cultural universal** is a behavior or pattern of thought taught by all cultures but expressed in a different way by each. For example, all of these countries practice a particular dominant religion, but not all practice the same religion.

Materials

- geography magazines, reference materials such as encyclopedias or other books, and/or Internet resources
- paper
- pencils
- other assorted materials depending on team project chosen

What to Do

1. Choose two or three partners. Your team should then choose one of the Southeast Asian countries to research. Each group should be sure to choose a different country so that all are represented.
2. Research these cultural universals for each country: government; economy; roles of men, women, and children; arts, crafts, drama, and music; religion; transportation; food; language; agriculture; holidays; games and recreation. You may add to or delete from this list, but be sure that all of your groups study the same cultural universals.
3. Discuss some of your discoveries, and then divide all the teams into two groups. Create a Venn diagram for each group that stresses similarities and differences. Work to identify common threads that run through the various cultures using the cultural universals you researched.
4. Create a visual presentation that illustrates part of your team's research. Your team could choose to portray the arts and present a drama, puppet, or musical performance. You could create replicas of crafts, fabric, or architectural designs. You could cook and serve a buffet displaying various foods from the country you researched. Be sure to choose different representations from group to group. The possibilities are limitless. Use your imagination!

CHAPTER 8

SOUTHEAST ASIA
GeoLab Activity 8 (continued)

Lab Activity Report

1. Compare the cultures researched and presented to the way of life in your own community. Have you observed that particular activity or trait where you live? How, where, and by whom?

   _____

2. What similarities or differences does your way of life have to that in Southeast Asia?

   _____

3. Is there anything you can take from your study of Southeast Asia that you would like to see included in your own life?

   _____

4. **Drawing Conclusions** Why do you think all cultures have cultural universals?

   _____

   _____

The world's smallest bear, the sun bear, is native to Southeast Asia. It is about four feet tall when standing and can weigh from 100 to 140 pounds, about the size of a large dog. Although small, the sun bear can be very dangerous.

Go A Step Further

Bamboo is grown all over Southeast Asia, and is an amazing, renewable resource. Bamboo is a well-known source for food and for basket weaving materials, but it has many other uses as well. Research to find at least 10 other uses for bamboo. If your teacher has access to bamboo, use some to create a musical instrument that is like one that might be used in Southeast Asia. (Note: Bamboo can be ordered at a reasonable cost on the Internet if no local garden center or craftstore has any available.)

Enrichment Activity 8

Sepak Takraw

Directions: Read the following article about the Indonesian sport, sepak takraw. Then complete the activity on a separate sheet of paper.

CHAPTER 8

Youth in Indonesia play many of the same sports as young people in the United States. They also play sports that are unique to Indonesia and the countries of Southeast Asia. One of those unique sports is sepak takraw, a fast-paced game in which the players use their feet and heads to move the ball. Sepak means "kick" and takraw means "woven ball." At one time, Indonesians wove bamboo or rattan to form the balls. For centuries, villagers gathered around in a circle. The players stood inside the circle and used their feet and heads to keep the ball from touching the ground. The object was to keep the ball in the air for as long as possible.

In the nineteenth century, the circle version of the game developed into a game that used a net. The net version of sepak takraw is similar to volleyball. Three players, known as the regu, make up the team. Today, the bamboo or rattan ball has been replaced with a plastic ball. The game is played on a badminton court. Badminton is a very popular game in Indonesia. Almost every school has badminton courts. Indonesians have adapted these courts to play sepak takraw.

Both the circle version and the net version of sepak takraw have become popular throughout Southeast Asia. A group from Southeast Asia now demonstrates the sport in other countries. Athletes from the United States, Canada, Great Britain, Finland, Germany, Puerto Rico, Colombia, Brazil, Australia, and New Zealand have begun to play the net version of the sport.

Sepak takraw shares many similarities with volleyball. A server serves the ball across the net and the opponents have three contacts to get the ball back over the net. Points are scored when the ball lands on the opponent's side of the court. Unlike volleyball, the players cannot hit the ball with their hands. In fact, they can use any part of their bodies except their hands. Players use their feet, legs, and head to play the ball. They may pass the ball to one of their teammates or they may hit the ball over the net. Spikes, digs, sets, and blocks are used in both sepak takraw and volleyball.

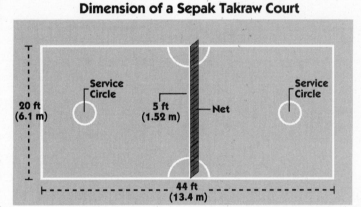

Dimension of a Sepak Takraw Court

Service Circle • 20 ft (6.1 m) • 5 ft (1.52 m) • Net • Service Circle • 44 ft (13.4 m)

Taking Another Look

1. **Making Inferences** You are forming a regu to play sepak takraw. What skills do you think the athletes on your regu will need?
2. **Creating a Diagram** Organize into a small group. Imagine that you meet someone from Indonesia who has never seen a baseball game. Create a diagram of a baseball diamond. Label the positions of the bases, and mark where each of the players stands on the field. Then prepare a short presentation using the diagram that explains how baseball is played.

Chapter 8, Section Resources

SECTIONS

SOUTHEAST ASIA

Guided Reading Activity 8-1

Mainland Southeast Asia

DIRECTIONS: Filling in the Blanks Reading the section and completing the sentences below will help you learn more about mainland Southeast Asia. Use your textbook to fill in the blanks.

Myanmar once was called **(1)** _____. Mountains are located on its **(2)** _____ and **(3)** _____ borders. About two-thirds of the people **(4)** _____.

Myanmar provides about 75 percent of the world's **(5)** _____. These forests are decreasing because of **(6)** _____. Myanmar is a **(7)** _____ country.

Thailand was once called **(8)** _____. It is the only Southeast Asian country that has never been a **(9)** _____ colony. Thailand still honors its **(10)** _____ _____. Thailand's main agricultural exports are **(11)** _____ and **(12)** _____. Thailand is one of the world's leading exporters of **(13)** _____ and **(14)** _____.

Laos is covered by **(15)** _____. This country is economically **(16)** _____. The country has **(17)** _____ in only a few cities. The government is **(18)** _____ and the people remain **(19)** _____ in religion.

Cambodia was a rich **(20)** _____ country for many years. The economy deteriorated because of harsh **(21)** _____ rule and years of **(22)** _____ war. The main religion in Cambodia is **(23)** _____.

Vietnam has the largest **(24)** _____ in mainland Southeast Asia. Most people belong to the **(25)** _____ ethnic group and are **(26)** _____ in religion.

Guided Reading Activity 8-2

Island Southeast Asia

DIRECTIONS: Outlining Reading the section and completing the outline below will help you learn more about the island countries of Southeast Asia. Refer to your textbook to fill in the blanks.

I. Indonesia is an _____ of more than 13,600 islands.

  A. It is made up of _____ major islands. They are:

  1. _____,

  2. _____, and

  3. _____.

  B. Indonesia has a _____ climate.

  C. Nearly half of Indonesians make a living in _____.

  D. Most Indonesians belong to the _____ ethnic group.

  E. Indonesia's main religions are _____, _____, _____,

  and _____.

II. Malaysia is made up of rain forests and _____.

  A. Malaysia is one of the world's leaders in exporting _____ and _____.

  B. _____ is the capital and largest city.

  C. Most people belong to the _____ ethnic group.

III. Singapore includes Singapore Island and _____ smaller islands.

  A. It is one of the world's most productive _____.

  B. The city of Singapore has one of the world's busiest _____.

  C. Most of Singapore's people are _____.

IV. Brunei

  A. About half of the nation's income comes from _____ and _____

  _____ exports.

  B. Brunei's _____ makes all political and economic decisions.

V. The Philippines include more than _____ islands.

  A. _____ _____ and _____ cover the landscape.

  B. Farmers build _____ _____ so that the land will hold more water.

  C. The Philippines is the only _____ country in Southeast Asia.

ANSWER KEY

3-A

Borders should match those on subsequent maps for this unit.

3-B

1. Indian Ocean
2. Xi River
3. Great Indian Desert
4. Taklimakan Desert
5. Yangtze River
6. Manchurian Plain
7. Himalaya
8. Mt. Everest
9. Mt. Fuji
10. Yellow Sea

3-C

1. Japan
2. India
3. China
4. North Korea
5. Indonesia
6. Mongolia
7. Vietnam
8. Myanmar
9. Nepal
10. Taiwan

3-D

1. Islamabad
2. New Delhi
3. Beijing
4. Tokyo
5. Yangon
6. Seoul
7. Ulaanbaatar
8. Jakarta
9. Manila
10. Hanoi

3-E

1. Mt. Everest, which has an elevation of 29,035 feet (8,850 m), and Mt. Fuji, which has an elevation of 12,388 feet (3,776 m), are shown on this profile.
2. Mt. Everest in located in Nepal (and Tibet); Mt. Fuji is located in Japan.

3. The Yellow Sea is shown on this profile. It is bordered by China, North Korea, and South Korea.
4. The Kunlun Shan also borders the Plateau of Tibet.
5. The Yangtze River and the Yellow River flow through the North China Plain.
6. This elevation profile runs west to east from approximately 28°N to 35°N latitude.
7. This profile runs through India, Nepal, China, South Korea, and Japan.

3-F

1. China
2. Japan
3. 210,000
4. China: 20.7%; India: 16.8%; Indonesia: 3.4%; Pakistan: 2.4%; Japan: 2.1%; Bangladesh: 2.2%
5. Han Chinese
6. 30%
7. 84%
8. 125
9. Conclusions will vary. Most students will note that people in China are relatively poor.
10. Since there are only three automobiles for every 1,000 people, few Chinese use an automobile everyday.

3-G

Ten Most Populous Countries in Asia— Major Exports and Imports
Bangladesh; Machinery
China; Machinery
1,033,000,000; Crude oil
Indonesia; 206,100,000
Machinery; Manufactured goods
48,081,000; Beans
Pakistan; 145,000,000
Philippines; Electronic equipment
Thailand; Manufactured goods
78,700,000; Machinery

1. China has the largest population in Asia; India has the second-largest population.

2. Machinery is imported by five countries shown on this table.
3. Bangladesh exports clothing, and Myanmar exports beans.
4. China both imports and exports machinery.

Economics and Geography Activity 3

1. The United States imported the most from Japan in 1998.
2. The United States exported the most to Japan in 1998.
3. The difference was the greatest with Taiwan. The United States imported $76,464.50 more than it exported.
4. The smallest difference was with Bangladesh.
5. The countries whose major exports are related to the clothing industry are Bangladesh, Taiwan, Indonesia, and Sri Lanka.
6. Malaysia, South Korea, and Singapore are major exporters of computer and electronic equipment.
7. The three countries that the U.S. imported the least from and their exports are: Bangladesh, clothing; Sri Lanka, textiles; and India, gems and jewelry.
8. Answers may vary but should include: As prices on imported goods increase, consumers may purchase alternative items in order not to pay increased prices. If less product is imported, the items may become scarce. Consumers who truly desire the items may spend money to purchase them and limit their spending in other areas. Students may mention that they are consumers of clothing, machinery, manufactured goods, or electronics from Asia. If the prices of these items increased, students would probably buy alternative products instead. If, for example, students love a brand of electronic products from South Korea, they may choose to pay higher prices for it instead of going without it.

History and Geography Activity 3

1. Fear of the Mongols motivated the Chinese to build the walls. The Mongols would sweep into China, terrorize the people, burn their houses, and steal whatever they could carry back north to Mongolia.
2. The walls did not keep the Mongols out because they were not connected. There were spaces between them that allowed the Mongols to enter China.
3. The Qin Dynasty Wall was begun in 221 B.C.
4. By 206 B.C. workers had constructed 1,550 miles (2,500 kilometers) of the Qin Dynasty Wall.
5. We know the Qin Dynasty Wall did not keep the Mongols out of China because Kublai Khan, a Mongol, not only invaded China, he became its emperor.
6. The Qin Dynasty Wall was built with packed mud; workers built the Great Wall using stone. Stone is a more permanent substance than mud.
7. Prompt students to consider who ordered the construction of the wall. Explain that Chinese peasants, or poor laborers, had to carry out the will of the emperor.
8. Students' answers may vary. They should mention natural barriers such as mountains, oceans, and deserts. For example, the Himalaya and thick forests have isolated Bhutan while Madagascar, surrounded by water, has also been isolated.
9. The Great Wall of China follows the contours of the mountains and ridges of northern China and is therefore not straight.
10. Students should use the reference maps in their textbook to help them locate and label the map correctly.
   a. The Yellow Sea prevented the wall from traveling farther to the east.

b. The Gobi is a natural barrier in the west.

Environmental Case Study 3

1. Its large population has grown too rapidly for the government to provide an adequate infrastructure.
2. Answers will vary but could include two of the following: cars, burning garbage, industrial wastes, and cooking on kerosene stoves.
3. Piped-in water reaches some households, but most people get most of their water from private wells. Poor people must buy bottled water.
4. It has begun to sink because people have taken so much water from the ground.
5. Answers will vary but could include the following: Most of Jakarta does not have a modern sewage system. Open ditches take wastewater, sometimes without treatment, to rivers or the sea.
6. Some people dump their garbage along the side of the street, while others burn it.
7. Answers will vary but could include the following: There are too many people. Good housing in the city is expensive and hard to find.
8. Answers will vary but could include two of the following: building roads, building public toilets, building health clinics, building schools, laying more water pipes, starting vehicle emissions tests, banning leaded gasoline, and putting in a new sewage system.

Citizenship Activity 3

Student answers to the Questions to Consider will vary. These questions require students to use examples from their daily lives and to critically think about issues that affect them. Students should answer the questions by using complete sentences and by supporting their opinions with logical arguments. Students should complete the Citizenship Activity Task by working individually and in groups. At the end of the project, have students review their work by discussing the difficulties they faced and how they resolved them. Encourage students to explain how they would improve their work if they did this project again.

World Literature Reading 3

The Long Season of Rain

1. Junehee says that her house, like all traditional Korean homes, lacks privacy.
2. Junehee's house is in the shape of a horseshoe.
3. The major difference between traditional Korean homes and houses or apartments in the United States is that all the rooms in Korean houses are not internally connected. One must put on shoes and go outside to go to different rooms. Most American homes have hallways and/or stairways that connect the rooms and floors.

Shabanu, Daughter of the Wind

1. Shabanu says the desert rises and falls like the Arabian Sea.
2. She sees no difference and, in fact, cannot tell where Pakistan ends and India begins.
3. Answers may vary but students should mention that when she thinks of leaving Cholistan, Shabanu's chest swells with a pain so deep it closes her throat and sends tears to her eyes. She also says she feels there is nowhere else so grand on Earth.
4. Answers may vary. Students may mention that Shabanu's family moves from place to place and their home is in the same place; Shabanu travels around on a camel and they travel in vehicles such as cars, buses, minivans, and so on; Shabanu's family has to get its water from a well and they get their water from taps in their homes; Shabanu lives in a desert and they may live in a city, on a farm, in a suburb, in the mountains, near the ocean, and so on.

ANSWER KEY

Vocabulary Activity 5
1. jute
2. cottage industry
3. subcontinent
4. monsoon
5. cyclone
6. pesticides
7. *dzong*
8. castes
9. reincarnation

Cooperative Learning Activity 5
Students should complete the Cooperative Group Process activities and questions and answer the Quick Check questions. Have students share their responses with their groups or with the class as a whole.

Chapter Map Activity 5
Use the reproducible maps in the classroom. You may wish to use the teacher strategies presented for this chapter or other map skills strategies of your own design.

Chapter Skills Activity 5
Practicing the Skill
1. ethnic groups of Sri Lanka and India
2. Indo-Aryans
3. Sri Lanka
4. 74%

Applying the Skill
Student circle graphs will vary. Check student circle graphs to make sure the graphs are in the correct format as shown by the circle graph on the page and in the student text.

Reteaching Activity 5
1. Pakistan
2. Sri Lanka
3. Bhutan
4. Bangladesh
5. India
6. Nepal

Critical Thinking Skills Activity 5
Applying the Skill
The following letters should be circled: A, C, F, and G.

Practicing the Skill
1. A
2. C
3. B
4. B

Map and Graph Skills Activity 5
Applying the Skill
1. miles and kilometers
2. about 150 miles (240 kilometers)
3. Agra
4. about 500 miles (800 kilometers)
5. Mumbai
6. Faisalabad
7. approximately 7 1/2 hours (It is about 375 miles from Kathmandu to Calcutta; dividing 375 [miles] by 50 [miles per hour] equals 7 1/2 hours.)
8. Most students will decide that it would be easier for them to hike 25 miles (40 kilometers) per day in Bangladesh than in Nepal, because the terrain in Nepal is much more mountainous than that of Bangladesh.

Practicing the Skill
1. C
2. B
3. C

Reading and Writing Skills Activity 5
Applying the Skill
1. Mohandas K. Gandhi
2. his delay in leaving Bombay due to the weather
3. The Indian Ocean is rough in June and July. A ship had just been sunk in a storm. His brother did not want him to risk the poor weather conditions.

4. Student answers will vary. Examples of student primary sources include a photo, a report card, an old newspaper clipping, a baptismal certificate, or an autobiography.
5. Student answers will vary. Correct answers will place into some historical context the primary source the student brought.

Practicing the Skill
1. A
2. D

GeoLab Activity 5
1. Students should include the Himalaya, Western Ghats, Eastern Ghats, Satpura Range, and possibly the Deccan Plateau.
2. Answers will vary, but students should realize that most cities are located on plains or plateaus, sometimes near hills, on or near fertile land and water.
3. The Karakoram Range and the Himalaya form India's northern border.
4. Low, fertile land near water helps to promote city growth. It is easier to travel and build in these kinds of areas.

Enrichment Activity 5
Box 3: India collides with the Asian plate.
Box 5: The earth's crust pushes up, forming the Himalaya.
Box 7: The Himalaya rise higher.
1. It ran into the Asian plate.
2. The Himalaya continue to increase in size.

Guided Reading Activity 5-1
1. A subcontinent is a large landmass that is a part of another continent but distinct from it.
2. Two mountain ranges, the Karakoram Range and the Himalaya form India's northern border.
3. It is warm or hot throughout the year.
4. Agriculture and industry are important to India's economy.
5. A cottage industry is a home- or village-based industry in which family members supply their own equipment to make goods.
6. Forests have been cleared, water and land have been polluted, and animal habitats have been destroyed.
7. The first Indian civilizations built cities in present-day Pakistan, along the Indus River valley.
8. Mohandas Gandhi led a nonviolent resistance movement to gain Indian independence.
9. Most people are Hindus. They believe it is wrong to kill any living thing. Cows are sacred, so they roam freely throughout India.
10. About 70 percent live in rural farming villages.

Guided Reading Activity 5-2
1. Muslim
2. cultures
3. water resources
4. Punjabi
5. Sindhi
6. rural villages
7. India
8. Brahmaputra
9. Ganges
10. farming
11. densely
12. poorest
13. Himalaya
14. farming
15. India
16. Himalaya
17. subsistence farmers
18. Dzonkha
19. farming
20. tea
21. Sinhalese

Vocabulary Activity 6
1. pagoda
2. typhoon
3. empire
4. calligraphy

5. nomad
6. consumer goods
7. yurt
8. invest
9. dynasty
10. fault
11. dike
12. communist state
13. high-technology industries—industries that produce computers and other kinds of electronic equipment

Cooperative Learning Activity 6

Students should complete the Cooperative Group Process activities and questions and answer the Quick Check questions. Have students share their responses with their groups or with the class as a whole.

Chapter Map Activity 6

Use the reproducible maps in the classroom. You may wish to use the teacher strategies presented for this chapter or other map skills strategies of your own design.

Chapter Skills Activity 6

Practicing the Skill

1. The Taiwanese elected a new president on March 18, 2000.
2. Taiwan has developed into a true democracy. The people of Taiwan have demonstrated that the will of the people of Taiwan cannot be coerced. The right of self-determination of Taiwan's people cannot be sabotaged. The new American president indeed will need a new China policy. A new United States China policy needs to be clear and must reflect the reality of the Taiwan Strait. The United States's "One China Policy" needs to be replaced by a "One China, One Taiwan Policy."
3. The purpose of the passage is to explain that the author feels that the new United States president should base his policies

toward acknowledging that Taiwan is its own nation, not just a part of China.

Applying the Skill

1. Student answers will vary. Check that the student understands what distinguishes a fact from an opinion. Ask students to hand in the editorial with this assignment.
2. Student answers will vary. Check that the student understands what distinguishes a fact from an opinion.
3. Student answers will vary. Read the editorial if necessary to make sure the student understood the editorial's purpose.

Reteaching Activity 6

China: B, C, F, G, J, M, N
Taiwan: D, H, K, O
Mongolia: A, E, I, L, O

Critical Thinking Skills Activity 6

Applying the Skill

A. Students should place check marks in front of 3, 4, 5, 6, 9, and 10. Students' answers will vary. Challenge them to evaluate the accuracy of the stereotypes by identifying exaggerations, negative or positive slants, and individual characteristics. Students should find that most stereotypes are inaccurate.
B. Students' answers will vary depending upon the movie, program, or book they choose. Their answers should reflect an understanding of stereotypes.

Practicing the Skill

1. C
2. D
3. C

Map and Graph Skills Activity 6

Applying the Skill

1. The largest percentage of workers are in agriculture.

2. Services make up the largest percentage of the Chinese economy, and about 26 percent of the workers have jobs there.

3. Agriculture is the smallest segment of the Chinese economy.

4. False. The graph shows that industry and service jobs account for about 50 percent of jobs in China, and agricultural jobs account for the other 50 percent.

5. Half of Chinese workers are farmers, but agriculture is the smallest part of the Chinese economy. Many students will be surprised that agriculture is not the largest segment of the economy, given the large number of Chinese who make their living as farmers. Some students may speculate that many farms and collectives barely produce enough to feed themselves; that farming is often difficult and inefficient in comparison to industry; that the Communist government spends more to develop industries; and so on.

6. Most agricultural activity takes place in northeastern and southeastern China, in the country's fertile plains. Western and northern China are mountainous regions not well suited to farming.

7. Answers will vary but should mention (a) the greater productivity of industrial and services workers than farmers and (b) the contrast in the far larger percentage of the labor force in agriculture and agriculture's output in the economy.

Practicing the Skill

1. C
2. B
3. D

Reading and Writing Skills Activity 6

Applying the Skill

1. Both articles describe the events at the beginning of the Tiananmen Square demonstrations.

2. The passage from *Modern China: A History* was written in 1994. The passage from *China: A New Revolution?* was written in 1990.

3. Student answers will vary. The passage from *Modern China* identifies the date of Hu Yaobang's death, the fact that the demonstrations began in honor of him, that the students were upset because the government had canceled their right to seek their own job after graduation, that thousands of students gathered in Tiananmen Square on April 17, and that more demonstrations followed. The passage from *China* mentions Hu Yaobang's death, the problem of corruption in the government, and the lack of movement toward democracy. It also describes that the students at Beijing University began the demonstrations by marching from the university to Tiananmen Square. These first demonstrations were not opposed by the government.

4. Student answers will vary. The first passage focuses on the students' anger at not being allowed to find their own jobs, while the second passage focuses on the broader message that the students wanted more democracy. The second passage mentions that university students all over China discussed political problems, while the first passage focuses on the actions of the students at Beijing University.

Practicing the Skill

1. D
2. B

GeoLab Activity 6

1. Smaller pieces take less time to cook.
2. Answers will vary according to the students' experiences. The bigger, thicker vegetables will take longer to cook.
3. The short cooking time means the fuel source will be conserved, and also because the food is meant to cook quickly. All the food needs to complete cooking at the same time for good taste and texture.

ANSWER KEY

Quick cooking also means better retention of nutrients in the vegetables.

4. Answers will vary, but students should realize that meat is very hard to purchase in China. It is expensive, and vegetables are more plentiful.

Enrichment Activity 6

1. An ink stick is made of soot and glue.
2. Water is placed in the inkstone's well. The ink stick is dipped into the water to moisten it. The artist uses the grinding area of the inkstone to rotate the ink stick. The ink flows into the well and mixes with the water. The water thickens and darkens as it becomes ink.
3. The artist carefully selects the brush and the paper or silk on which the painting will be made.
4. Answers will vary. Making ink sticks is an art form. The best quality sticks result in the best quality ink. Since the liquid ink is created by the artist as the first step in the painting, the better the quality of the stick, the fewer rotations are needed to create the ink. The artist can concentrate on the painting and a better quality of painting may result.

Guided Reading Activity 6-1

1. True.
2. False. There are high plateaus and deserts.
3. True.
4. True.
5. False. They also face the danger of floods.
6. False. The government has strong control over the economy.
7. True.
8. False. China's economic growth has hurt the nation's environment by polluting the air and water.
9. True.

Guided Reading Activity 6-2

1. one-fifth
2. Han Chinese
3. foreign invaders
4. Great Wall of China
5. Kongfuzi
6. honest
7. brave
8. Laozi
9. Daoism
10. 1700s
11. 1800s
12. trade
13. republic
14. 1949
15. Deng Xiaoping
16. human rights
17. Tibet
18. rural
19. community centers
20. cities

Guided Reading Activity 6-3

I.
  A. island
    1. mountains
    2. plains
    3. mild
  B. prosperous
    1. high-technology
    2. Asian neighbors
  C. Agriculture
  D. China's
    1. Japan
    2. China
    3. Nationalists
    4. democracy

II.
  A. landlocked
    1. mountains, plateaus
    2. bleak
    3. steppes
  B. Blue Sky
  C. nomads
  D. Genghis Khan
    1. land empire
    2. 1300s
  E. Buddhism

ANSWER KEY

Vocabulary Activity 7
1. clan
2. samurai
3. shogun
4. constitutional monarchy
5. tsunami
6. archipelago
7. megalopolis
8. intensive cultivation
9. monsoon

Cooperative Learning Activity 7
Students should complete the Cooperative Group Process activities and questions and answer the Quick Check questions. Have students share their responses with their groups or with the class as a whole.

Chapter Map Activity 7
Use the reproducible maps in the classroom. You may wish to use the teacher strategies presented for this chapter or other map skills strategies of your own design.

Chapter Skills Activity 7

Practicing the Skill
1. the religions of North Korea and South Korea
2. Buddhism and Christianity
3. South Korea

Applying the Skill
Student circle graphs will vary. Check the graphs to be sure they are in the correct format as in the "Practicing the Skill" section of this worksheet.

1. Student answers will vary. Check to make sure the circle graph agrees with the student's answer.
2. Student answers will vary. Check student answers for a well thought-out comparison.

Reteaching Activity 7
Japan: A, F, G, I, J, K, O, P, Q
North Korea: B, C, D, E, L, M, R
South Korea: B, D, H, M, N

Critical Thinking Skills Activity 7

Applying the Skill
- Cause: Soviet Union troops took over the north and American troops occupied the south.
- Effect: North Korea struggles with poverty and food shortage; religion is discouraged.
- Effect: South Korea's economy is strong; religion is freely practiced.

Practicing the Skill
1. B
2. D

Map and Graph Skills Activity 7

Applying the Skill
1. China has the largest population.
2. Singapore has the smallest population.
3. Taiwan
4. False
5. Japan is more densely populated. Although it is similar in size to Malaysia, Japan has about six times the number of people.
6. Students should compare the population percentages with the land area of the countries to come up with a list of countries ranked from greatest to least population densities. Students should then find the actual population densities (see list below) and compare their lists to the actual numbers. Students should explain their processes and why their guesses were right or wrong.

Population Densities of Asian Pacific Rim Countries:
Singapore: 16,732 per sq. mi. (6,471 per sq. km)
Taiwan: 1,583 per sq. mi. (611 per sq. km)
South Korea: 1,226 per sq. mi. (473 per sq. km)
Japan: 869 per sq. mi. (335 per sq. km)

China: 339 per sq. mi. (131 per sq. km)
Malaysia: 178 per sq. mi. (69 per sq. km)

Practicing the Skill
1. C
2. A
3. B

Reading and Writing Skills Activity 7

Applying the Skill

1. Student answers will vary. Correct answers may include:
   —Computer databases—You can research the current politics in Japan by searching a library's computer database, using the key words *Japan* and *politics*. When you receive the search results, be sure to narrow your focus to only the most recent articles.
   —*Readers' Guide to Periodical Literature*—You can find recent articles by looking for *Japanese politics* in the most recent print edition of the *Readers' Guide*.
   —Internet—You can do a key word search on a search engine using *Japan* and *politics*. Once you get the search results, click on links that are closely related to your topic and that are recent. Be sure to evaluate the reliability of Internet information.
2. Student answers will vary. Correct answers may include:
   —Computer databases—You can research Japanese military strategy in World War II by searching a library's computer database, using the key words *Japan, World War II, military,* and/or *strategy,* depending on the database you use. You do not have to narrow your focus to only the most recent articles.
   —*Readers' Guide to Periodical Literature*—You can find articles by looking for *Japan, World War II, military,* and/or *strategy.* You might also try looking in the hardbound *Readers' Guides* for the

years during which World War II was fought in the Pacific theater.
   —Microfilm and microfiche—To find the older articles that you researched using a computer database and the *Readers' Guide,* you may have to search through the library's microfilm and microfiche collections.
   —Internet—You can do a key word search on a search engine using *Japan, World War II, military,* and/or *strategy.* Once you get the search results, click on links that are closely related to your topic. These do not necessarily have to be recent, but they should be reliable.
3. Student answers will vary. Correct answers may include:
   —Computer databases—You can search a library's computer database, using the key words *North Korea* and *South Korea.* When you receive the search results, be sure to narrow your focus to only the most recent articles that closely relate to your topic.
   —*Readers' Guide to Periodical Literature*—You can find recent articles by looking for *North Korea* and *South Korea* in the most recent print edition of the *Readers' Guide.*
   —Internet—You can do a key word search on a search engine using *North Korea* and *South Korea.* Once you get the search results, click on links that are closely related to your topic and that are recent and reliable.
4. Student answers will vary. Correct answers may include:
   —Computer databases—You can search a library's computer database, using the key words *South Korea* and *economy.* When you receive the search results, be sure to narrow your focus to only the most recent articles that closely relate to your topic.
   —*Readers' Guide to Periodical Literature*—You can find recent articles by looking

for *South Korea* and *economy* in the most recent print edition of the *Readers' Guide.*

—Internet—You can do a key word search on a search engine using *South Korea* and *economy.* Once you get the search results, click on links that are closely related to your topic and that are recent and reliable.

Practicing the Skill

1. D
2. B

GeoLab Activity 7

1. Answers will vary, but students who read it should have had some reaction to the story on an emotional level.
2. Answers will vary depending on the individual student, but students should give reasons to support their statements.
3. The color can then add dimension and definition to the art piece. It can also indicate inside/outside relationships.
4. Answers will vary, but students should note that paper folding seems like such a simple craft, yet it is quite intricate and can demand great skill. Even though it uses a single, ordinary material, it can be very expressive.

Enrichment Activity 7

1. An earthquake on the ocean floor causes a tsunami.
2. Energy from the earthquake rises directly above the fault. The energy begins the formation of the sea waves. The waves grow as the ocean floor becomes shallower. By the time the wave reaches land, the tsunami is a huge wave that floods the coastal area.
3. Diary entries will vary but might include: fear of being buried in rubble; concern for friends and family; need to know information about the extent of the damage; concern over water and food supply; fear of fire, downed electric lines, inability of

rescue crews to reach people in need; concern about immediate need for food and medical attention. (You may want to encourage students to research the Kobe earthquake for more information.)

4. Natural dangers facing the Japanese include strong earthquakes, tsunamis, and volcanic eruptions.

Guided Reading Activity 7-1

1. Japan lies on the Ring of Fire, an area where the earth's crust often shifts, causing earthquakes and tsunamis.
2. Japan's land area is made up of four main islands and thousands of smaller ones.
3. Japan is an industrial giant known for the variety and quality of its manufactured goods.
4. Japan's farmers use fertilizers and modern machinery, and practice intensive cultivation in which crops are grown on every piece of available land.
5. Japan imports few finished goods, and other countries feel that Japan's trade restrictions are unfair. Japan also faces environmental problems.
6. The Japanese trace their ancestry to various clans that lived on the islands.
7. From the late 1100s to the 1860s, shoguns or military leaders ruled Japan.
8. Most crowd into urban areas on the coastal plains.
9. Shinto and Buddhism teach respect for nature, love for simple things, and concern for cleanliness and good manners.
10. Sumo, judo, and karate have their origins in the past.

Guided Reading Activity 7-2

1. True.
2. False. Korea was ruled by Japan until the end of World War II.
3. True.
4. False. The Korean War ended without a peace treaty, and two separate countries had developed.

ANSWER KEY

5. True.

6. False. Manufacturing and trade dominate South Korea's economy.

7. False. Farming does not provide enough food for the whole country. Famines have recently occurred.

8. True.

9. False. Mountains run only through the center of the country.

10. True.

Vocabulary Activity 8

1. plate
2. free port
3. socialism
4. precious gems
5. terraced fields
6. monsoons
7. Strait
8. delta
9. civil war
10. deforestation

Cooperative Learning Activity 8

Students should complete the Cooperative Group Process activities and questions and answer the Quick Check questions. Have students share their responses with their groups or with the class as a whole.

Chapter Map Activity 8

Use the reproducible maps in the classroom. You may wish to use the teacher strategies presented for this chapter or other map skills strategies of your own design.

Chapter Skills Activity 8

Practicing the Skill

1. Java in Indonesia
2. 300 m, 600 m, 1,500 m
3. a flatter, gradual slope; a steep slope

Applying the Skill

1. Obtain a contour map of your state. Check student answers on this map.

2. Check student answers on the contour map of your state.

3. Check student answers on the contour map of your state.

Reteaching Activity 8

1. Thailand
2. Brunei
3. Malaysia
4. Singapore
5. Laos
6. Philippines
7. Vietnam
8. Indonesia
9. Myanmar
10. Cambodia

Critical Thinking Skills Activity 8

Applying the Skill

1. According to Senator Fulbright, Vietnam was not a threat to our own country's security, and the United States should have let the people of Vietnam choose the political system they wanted.

2. Davidson believes the United States was justified in entering the war because a communist state threatened the democracy of South Vietnam.

3. Senator Fulbright did not think the United States should have fought in the Vietnam War, even if it meant protecting a democratic country. Davidson thought the United States should have fought in Vietnam for moral reasons because the United States was trying to protect another democratic country.

4. Answers will vary. Students can agree or disagree for logical reasons. They may be influenced by Davidson, who had been a veteran of three wars, or Fulbright, who had been a United States senator.

Practicing the Skill

1. B
2. A
3. C
4. D

ANSWER KEY

Map and Graph Skills Activity 8

Applying the Skill

1. Buddhism
2. Three Southeast Asian countries are primarily Muslim: Malaysia, Indonesia, and Brunei.
3. The Philippines is the only Southeast Asian country in which Christianity is the predominant religion.
4. Buddhism
5. False. The predominant religion of Cambodia is Buddhism, while the predominant religion of Malaysia is Islam.
6. Buddhism is the predominant religion on the mainland of Southeast Asia; other religions become more prominent away from the mainland.
7. Responses may vary depending on sources used by students. Generally, the following answers should be found.
   Cambodia: Islam, others
   Laos: Christianity, Animist religions
   Vietnam: Christianity, Islam, others
   Thailand: Islam, others
   Myanmar: Islam, Christianity, others
   Malaysia: Buddhism, Confucianism, others
   Philippines: Islam, others
   Indonesia: Christianity, Hinduism, Buddhism
   Singapore: Christianity, Islam, others
   Brunei: Buddhism, Christianity, others

Practicing the Skill

1. D
2. B
3. C
4. A

Reading and Writing Skills Activity 8

Applying the Skill

1. general encyclopedias and government publications; If the student has specific knowledge of a specialized encyclopedia, that answer would also be acceptable.
2. general encyclopedias, atlases (atlas of explorers), biographical references
3. general encyclopedias, specialized encyclopedias, atlases (atlas of natural resources), almanacs and yearbooks
4. general encyclopedias, atlases (historical atlas), biographical references
5. general encyclopedias, atlases (historical atlas), almanacs and yearbooks, and government publications

Practicing the Skill

1. A
2. C

GeoLab Activity 8

1. Students will react differently to this question depending on what they studied and where they live. They might react differently if they live in a community with an Asian population in which particular customs are observed than if they live in a community with less diversity.
2. Students should recognize that religion, arts, and politics are components of all cultures from the family level to the national level. They may want to think, however, about the time or commitment given to similar activities in different societies. For example, it may be important to have dinner with the family, but is it "eat and run" or is it a time to spend together, an occasion to savor?
3. Answers will vary depending on the interest of the students. Perhaps they would like to have some of the architecture nearby to enjoy. Perhaps they wish a particular food were more readily available. They should be able to articulate a reasonable answer.
4. Students' answers will probably suggest that all people have behavior patterns and ways of living that have been influenced by the physical geography and contact with other people.

ANSWER KEY

Enrichment Activity 8

1. Answers will vary. Students may mention physical skills such as the ability to jump, kick, and maintain one's balance. They may also mention other skills such as the ability to work together on a team or the ability to plan and execute plays.
2. Group presentations will vary. The baseball diagram should clearly label the three bases, home plate, and the pitcher's mound. The nine players on the field should be properly labeled. Encourage groups to be creative, as well as accurate, in explaining how baseball is played.

Guided Reading Activity 8-1

1. Burma
2. western
3. eastern
4. farm
5. teakwood
6. deforestation
7. socialist
8. Siam
9. European
10. royal family
11. rubber
12. teakwood
13. tin
14. gemstones
15. mountains
16. poor
17. electricity
18. communist
19. Buddhists
20. farming
21. Communist
22. civil
23. Buddhism
24. population
25. Vietnamese
26. Buddhists

Guided Reading Activity 8-2

I. archipelago
   A. three
      1. Sumatra
      2. Java
      3. Celebes
   B. tropical
   C. agriculture
   D. Malay
   E. Islam, Christianity, Buddhism, Hinduism
II. mountains
   A. rubber, palm oil
   B. Kuala Lumpur
   C. Malay
III. 58
   A. economies
   B. harbors
   C. Chinese
IV.
   A. oil, natural gas
   B. sultan
V. 7,000
   A. volcanic mountains, forests
   B. terraced fields
   C. Christian

TEACHER NOTES

TEACHER NOTES